July 2001

Geographic information system (GIS) users have demonstrated boundless creativity in implementing ESRI's software programs, and this energy is reflected in each edition of the ESRI® Map Book. Since 1984, the book has served as an annual recognition of these outstanding and diverse accomplishments such as improving agricultural practices, assessing hazard risks, optimizing business opportunities, conserving resources, making long-term predictions, and unraveling the mysteries of outer space.

Initially acknowledged as an important tool for integrating and analyzing spatial information, GIS emerged as a powerful technology for coordinating the work of an organization around a common, shared geographic database. Today, GIS is providing society with a way to view the whole picture rather than just glimpse the fragments. As we review these maps and the work of the GIS community, we can imagine an evolving architecture that will enable groups of organizations to connect and share data and applications as network-based services.

The architecture of GIS for the future is focusing on creating a global framework that integrates the physical, social, biological, and environmental aspects of life. Based on an open environment and a distributed data management technology, these new, network-based geographic services are already showing up in thousands of organizations that have realized the value of cooperation and sharing. At ESRI, we are developing and testing systems to support this vision and provide our users with exciting opportunities for bringing the world together.

The ESRI Map Book acknowledges just a small portion of the terrific work coming from GIS professionals. You can view the maps in this book along with other GIS maps online at http://www.esri.com/mapgallery/.

Warm regards,

Jack Dangermond

Table of Contents

Soil and Climate Maps for the Heriot District

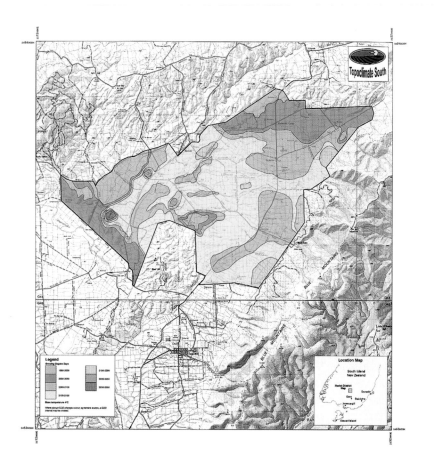

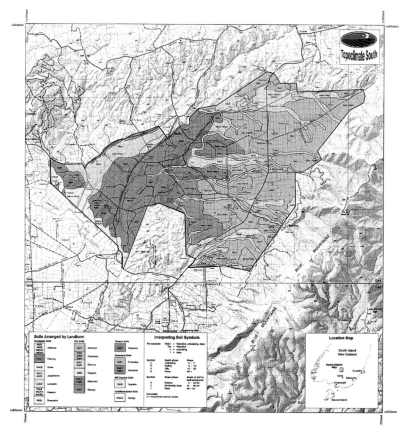

Topoclimate South
Mataura, New Zealand
Institute of Geological & Nuclear
Sciences, Ltd.
Dunedin, New Zealand

By S.T. Carrick, L.L. Eyre,
G.K. Hutchinson, P.D. McIntosh,
B. Morrison, K. Richards,
and W.H. Risk

Contact
Gary Hutchinson
garyh@topoclimate-south.co.nz

Software
ArcInfo™ 7.2.1 and 8.0.1 and
CorelDRAW

Hardware
Sun SPARC 20 UNIX workstation and
Windows NT

Printer
HP DesignJet 1050

Data Source(s)
Terralink NZ and Topoclimate South

Map Type
Inventory

The primary goal of the Topoclimate South project is to obtain detailed information about the climate and soils of the southern region of New Zealand, which has a moist, cool, temperate climate. This data will assist farmers, consultants, agribusiness managers, and other land users as they make land use decisions. The maps are at a 1:50,000 scale and identify soil and climate variations at a farm scale. The Heriot maps are part of a set of 35 maps that are being produced over a three-year period.

Soil mapping involves taking field observations to a one-meter depth at a frequency of about one observation per 20 hectares. This enables an interpretation of the variation in soil properties with similar points grouped together in a soil map unit. Each map unit is given a symbol and name, which is determined by using the New Zealand soil classification.

Climate data collected includes soil and air temperatures, which are measured by data loggers, established every 200–300 hectares on representative topographic landscape areas. The loggers remain at each site for one year. The results are correlated with records from the nearest long-term weather station with a 30-year temperature record constructed for each measurement site. Annual long-term heat pattern maps group together areas receiving a similar amount of heat. Other data, such as seasonal heat patterns, frequency and severity of frost, and maximum temperatures, can also be constructed.

Softwood Joint Venture Map—Kamona Plantation

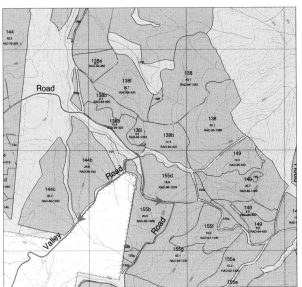

Plantation Series Map—Scamander Plantation

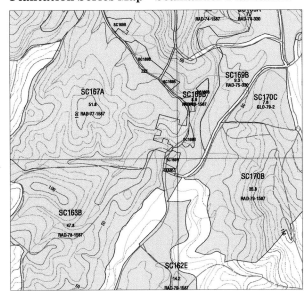

Land Tenure—1:500,000

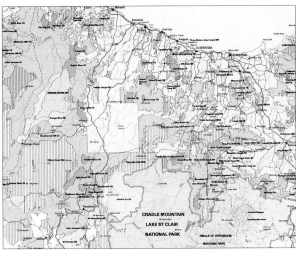

Photointerpreted Forest Type Map—Parkham

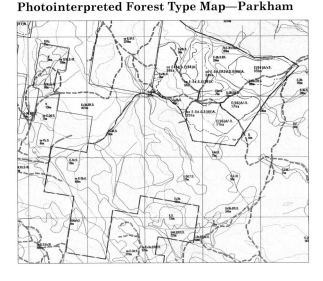

Hobart, Tasmania, Australia

By Forestry Tasmania Resources Branch (Mapping)

Contact
Chief Cartographer
forestry.tasmania@forestrytas.com.au
Software
ArcInfo 7.2.1 and 8 and PhotoGIS Version 2.2
Hardware
Sun Ultra Enterprise 250
Printer
HP DesignJet 755CM
Data Source(s)
Plantation data sourced from original ground surveys, field data, and global positioning system (GPS); topographical data from the Tasmanian state mapping agency; Tasmania Department of Primary Industry Water and Energy; Forestry Tasmania; and aerial photography
Map Type
Automation and Communication/ Cartography

Softwood Joint Venture Map—Kamona Plantation

In 1998, Forestry Tasmania (FT) was negotiating with a number of organizations to enter into a softwood joint venture (SJV) for the softwood plantations it owned and managed. This map was designed to show prospective SJV partners a tour route with examples of the softwood plantation and the age and density of each stand.

Plantation Series Map—Scamander Plantation

In 1989, FT began a project that involved digitally capturing its map series detail, automating the production of the series maps using ArcInfo. The goal was to produce a similar product (except using color) that had been available in a monochrome hard-copy format.

Land Tenure—1:500,000

The thematic map, Land Tenure, shows land status and covers the entire state of Tasmania. It is used by officers of Forestry Tasmania and the public.

Photointerpreted Forest Type Map—Parkham

Forest types are coded by photointerpreters into Forestry Tasmania's standard classifications indicating type of forest, height, and density. The forest type classification is based on forest management and inventory considerations rather than scientific communities.

The Hess Collection Winery—Veeder Hill Vineyard Viticulture Map

VESTRA Resources, Inc.
Redding, California

*By Richard Camera, Dean Roczen,
and Seth Schwebs*

Contact
Jamie Carothers
jamie@vestra.com

Software
ArcView® GIS 3.2 and ArcView
Spatial Analyst 2

Hardware
Windows NT

Printer
HP DesignJet 2500CP

Data Source(s)
Digital elevation model and ArcView
GIS shapefiles by VESTRA Resources,
Inc., and vineyard data by the Hess
Collection Winery

Map Type
Decision/Planning

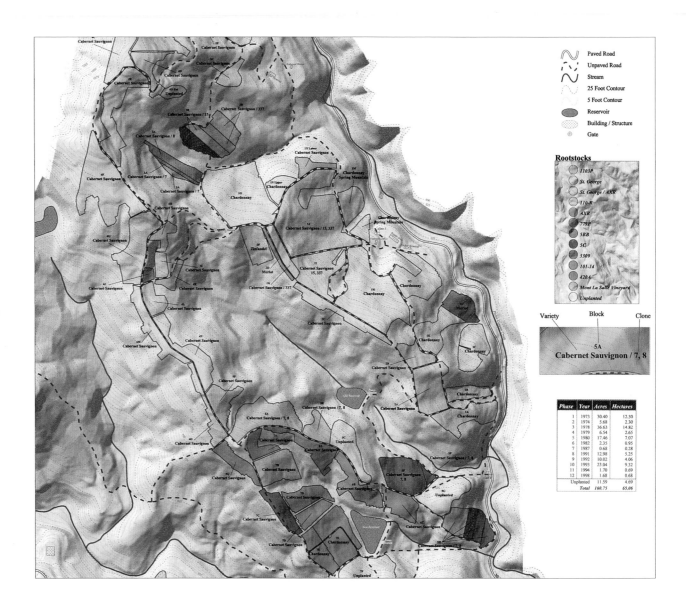

The Hess Collection is an ultra-premium winery based in Napa Valley, California, with six major vineyard estates. With more than 1,100 acres of wine grape acreage, GIS provides vineyard managers with a method to organize information and analyze their vineyard properties for better fruit quality, added efficiency, and long-term record keeping.

The Hess Collection's custom GIS is built on a foundation that begins with precision photogrammetry and orthophotography. This ensures that topography and feature identification is accurate enough to be appropriately used to support vineyard development and management, where development activities are locally regulated and crop management inputs need to be precise.

Using the orthophotography (and often GPS data capture) and the winery's own vineyard management records, a GIS database was built and maintained by both VESTRA Resources and winery managers. ArcView Desktop GIS software is used at the winery headquarters to make day-to-day maps that display important management data ranging from viticultural information to the location of underground irrigation facilities.

Vineyard maps are proving invaluable to Hess Collection staff at all decision levels. Vineyard managers and winemakers use GIS to make more informed and more precise decisions. The base GIS assists in satisfying local permitting requirements and vineyard development and planting selections. Hess Collection also integrates multispectral imagery products to help field management maintain and improve grape/wine quality goals. This information base reaches even further as it is used to support wine sales and marketing efforts.

Mapping Environmental Consequences of Conversion to Organic Farming

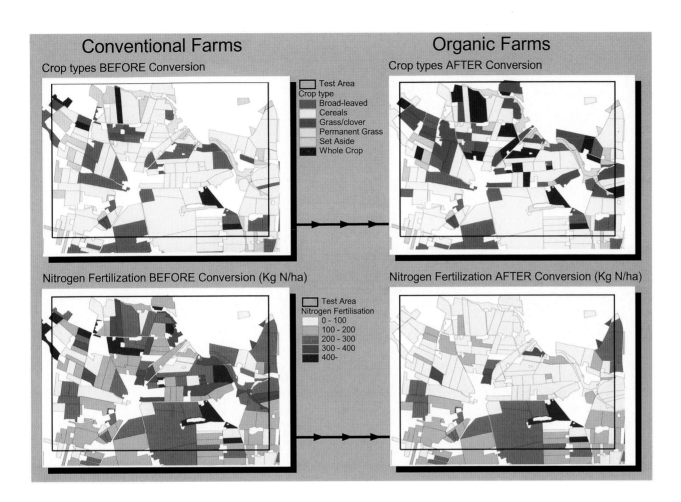

Danish Institute of Agricultural Sciences, Department of Agricultural Systems
Tjele, Denmark

By Tommy Dalgaard, Tove Heidmann, and Birgit M. Rasmussen

Contact
Birgit Rasmussen
birgitm.rasmussen@agrsci.dk

Software
ArcView GIS 3.1
Hardware
Windows NT
Printer
HP DesignJet 2500C
Data Source(s)
Danish Institute of Agricultural Sciences
Map Type
Modeling/Analytical

Pollution of groundwater-based drinking supplies is an increasing problem in many European countries including Denmark. Policy makers at the county or national level need reliable information on which to base decisions for reducing nitrogen leaching in environmentally sensitive areas (ESA).

Organic agriculture has been promoted in the expectation that the adverse effects on the environment are not as great as with conventional farming. A conversion to organic agriculture can be implemented using different strategies. In this project, four conversion scenarios were applied to a case study area to evaluate the effects on nitrate leaching with the intention of illustrating how GIS can be used to analyze the effect of different policy initiatives.

The case study area covers 2,000 hectares of agricultural land on sandy or loamy soils and includes conventional dairy, arable (stockless), pig, and mixed farms. Four possible outcomes necessary to achieve conversion of 25 percent of the area to organic farming were analyzed.

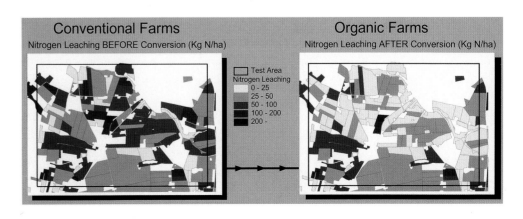

The Pacific Lumber Company's Habitat Conservation Plan

Pacific Lumber Company
Scotia, California

*By Todd Flackus, Alan Foreman,
Tim Spear, and Paul Vincent*

Contact
Paul Vincent
scopac@northcoast.com
Software
ArcInfo 8.0.1
Hardware
Windows NT and UNIX workstation
Printer
HP DesignJet 2500CP
Data Source(s)
In-house data acquisition, U.S.
Geological Survey, and the State of
California
Map Type
Decision/Planning

PALCOs Habitat Conservation Plan

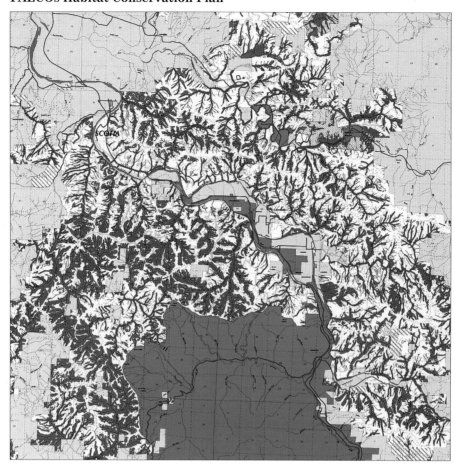

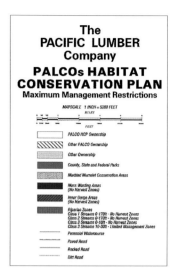

On March 1, 1999, the Pacific Lumber Company made a historic agreement with state and federal government to sell the largest old-growth redwood grove left in private ownership, the Headwaters Forest. As part of that agreement, Pacific Lumber will manage the rest of its commercial forestlands under a Habitat Conservation Plan (HCP), which provides the most protective environmental standards ever applied to any large, privately owned commercial forestlands. This HCP includes protection for wildlife, streams, land, and the trees. This map details some of the maximum management restrictions under the HCP. These and other protection guidelines must be followed for the duration of the HCP (50 years).

The Marbled Murrelet Conservation areas contain other fragmented, smaller old-growth redwood forests, which are off-limits to most management activities (no harvesting). The riparian buffers are made up of several buffers with high restrictive management practices. These buffers contain no-harvest inner buffers on all stream classifications and light selection to no-harvest on outer buffers. The mass wasting areas are areas that have landslides or the potential for landslide activity. These areas have no-harvest management restrictions associated with them. The inner gorges are steep areas immediately adjacent to stream courses with severe management restrictions.

A few of the coverages produced for this map are modeled coverages. The stream classification coverage was modeled using flow direction and flow accumulation with U.S. Geological Survey 30-meter digital elevation models. The mass wasting areas are also modeled and based on four different geologic features—soils, slope, geology, and geomorphology.

Forest Management of Lands Adjacent to the Headwaters Reserve

■	**Virgin Old Growth**
■	**Mixed Old Growth/Young Growth**
■	**Young Growth**
□	**Pacific Lumber Co. - excluding Headwaters (Prior to the Headwaters Transaction)**
⠿	**Headwaters Reserve**
▨	**Timber Harvest Plan 97-520HUM (California State Approved)**
▧	**Previous Timber Harvest Plans Elk River Timber Lands Only (Previous Owner)**
〜	**Headwaters Reserve Boundary**
〜	**Former ERTC Land Acquistion Boundary**

Map and Analysis by Paul Vincent

Painted Relief Map of Southern Humboldt County, California

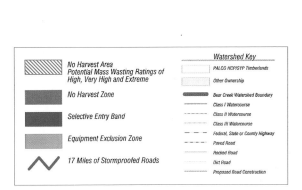

Bear Creek Watershed—PALCOs Habitat Conservation Plan Interim Prescriptions

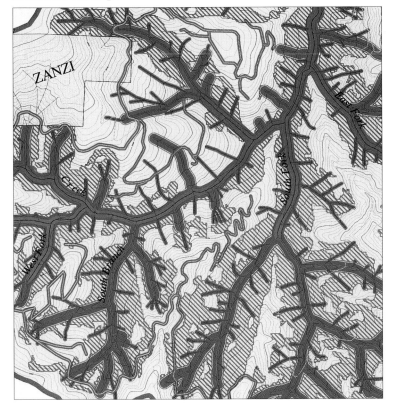

▨	No Harvest Area Potential Mass Wasting Ratings of High, Very High and Extreme		Watershed Key
■	No Harvest Zone		PALCO HCP/SYP Timberlands
■	Selective Entry Band		Other Ownership
■	Equipment Exclusion Zone		Bear Creek Watershed Boundary
〜	17 Miles of Stormproofed Roads		Class I Watercourse

Watershed Key:
- PALCO HCP/SYP Timberlands
- Other Ownership
- Bear Creek Watershed Boundary
- Class I Watercourse
- Class II Watercourse
- Class III Watercourse
- Federal, State or County Highway
- Paved Road
- Rocked Road
- Dirt Road
- Proposed Road Construction

Election Methods, by County
USA TODAY
Washington, D.C.

By Dave Merrill, Paul Overberg,
Frank Pompa, and April Umminger

Contact
Paul Overberg
poverberg@usatoday.com
Software
ArcView GIS 3.2 and Macromedia
Freehand 8
Hardware
IBM Intellistation M Pro and
Macintosh G3
Printer
Commercial offset web presses using
30-pound newsprint
Data Source(s)
In-house and survey by Election Data
Services Inc., Washington, D.C.
Map Type
Communication/Cartography

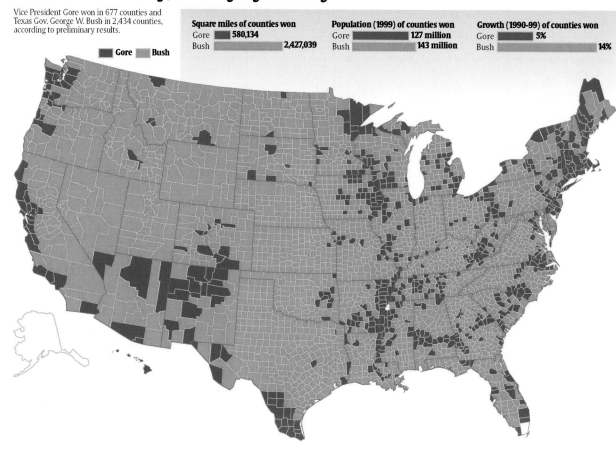

The vote Tuesday, county by county

Vice President Gore won in 677 counties and
Texas Gov. George W. Bush in 2,434 counties,
according to preliminary results.

Gore | Bush

Square miles of counties won		Population (1999) of counties won		Growth (1990-99) of counties won	
Gore	580,134	Gore	127 million	Gore	5%
Bush	2,427,039	Bush	143 million	Bush	14%

The extraordinary U.S. presidential election of November 7, 2000, drew national attention to voting mechanics and procedures. The Election Methods map was published in *USA TODAY* on November 14 as part of daily news coverage of the vote-counting controversy. It was also published on the Web in the early hours of that morning at www.USATODAY.com.

In print, it was sized at 7.25 inches by 9.25 inches to allow sufficient resolution of the smallest eastern counties. The map was produced from data compiled after the 1998 national election by Election Data Services, a Washington, D.C., election consulting firm and an ESRI reseller. The map passed three tests that *USA TODAY* uses to determine if a county-level U.S. map should be published: Does it tell a story? Does it reveal national and regional patterns? And, can it be rendered so that any of 5.5 million readers can find any particular county of personal interest?

The Vote Tuesday map was produced in a very short time using Associated Press's MapShop, a joint venture of the Associated Press and ESRI. It got extensive television coverage, and the map's very simplicity reveals all sorts of deeper patterns.

Election methods, by county

U.S. counties use many voting methods. In the 1998 elections, nearly 20% of counties used punch cards, such as the ones in dispute in Florida.

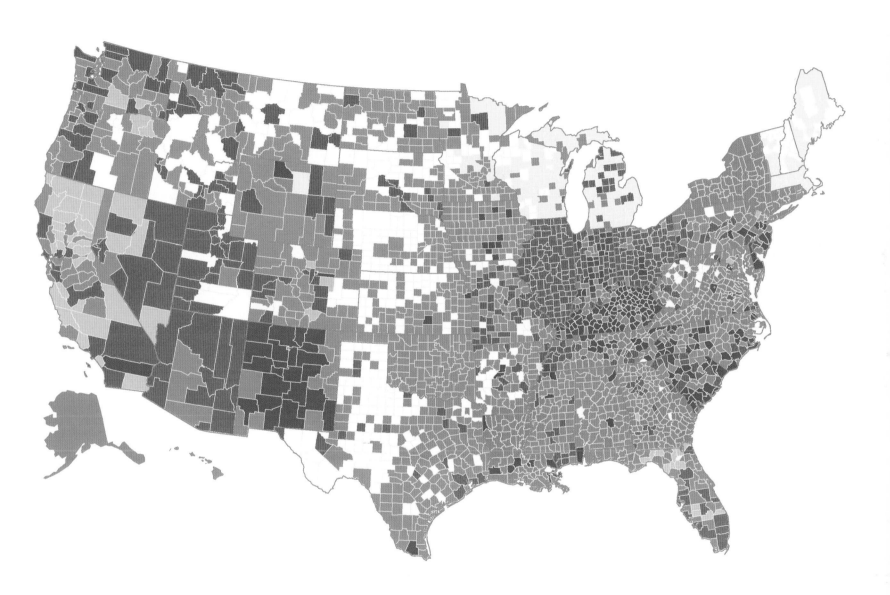

Voting methods, by county, in the 1998 elections:

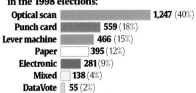

Method	Count	Percent
Optical scan	1,247	(40%)
Punch card	559	(18%)
Lever machine	466	(15%)
Paper	395	(12%)
Electronic	281	(9%)
Mixed	138	(4%)
DataVote	55	(2%)

Ways to vote:

 Optical scan: Voters indicate choices by shading empty or open rectangles, circles, ovals or arrows. Ballots are tabulated by scanner machines.

 Punch card: Voters insert blank cards into machines that list ballot choices. Then they punch out pre-scored holes to record their votes.

 DataVote: Voters punch holes next to choices printed on a ballot card.

 Lever machine: Voters push small levers to indicate choices. Then they pull a different, larger lever to record their votes. No longer manufactured.

 Electronic: Voters touch computer screens or push buttons to record their votes automatically.

 Paper: Voters mark boxes next to their choices and drop ballots into a sealed box.

Mixed: A combination of methods.

Risk Maps

Catastrophic Risk in the United States

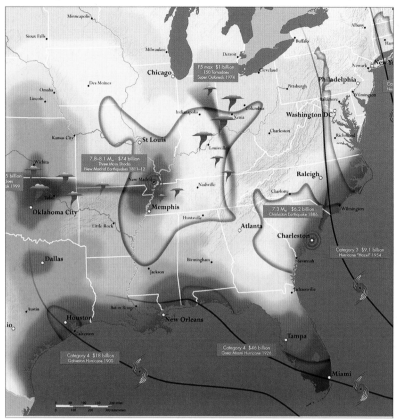

European Flood Risk

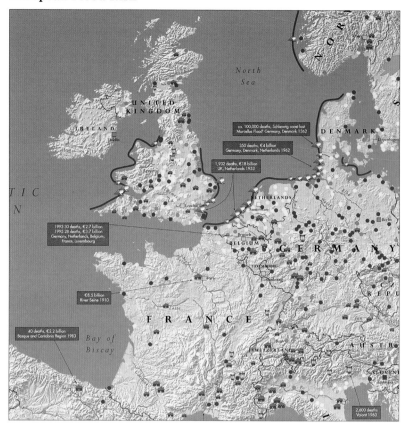

Risk Management Solutions Inc.
Newark, California

*By David Carttar, Laurie Johnson,
and Stacey Wright*

Contact
Richard White
richardw@rms.com
Software
ArcView GIS, ArcView Spatial Analyst,
Macromedia Freehand, Adobe
Photoshop, Adobe Illustrator,
and Quark Express
Hardware
Windows NT and Macintosh
Printer
Pass color web press
Data Source(s)
Various internal and external
data sets
Map Type
Modeling/Analytical

Catastrophic Risk in the United States

The four most costly insured hazards in the United States are earthquakes, hurricanes, tornadoes, and hailstorms. This map represents the combined relative risk of these hazards across the entire United States. Risk is depicted as the average annual loss (AAL) to a representative unit of residential exposure as measured by Risk Management Solutions' (RMS) RiskLink® catastrophe modeling technology. This is the first published map to enable the comparison of risk across perils and geographies using AAL as a fully convertible currency of risk.

European Flood Risk

Floods are the most costly natural disaster in Europe. Flood risk is highly localized and, as a result, difficult to quantify. This map represents the relative flood risk in Europe modeled for five flood types—river flood, flash flood, dam burst, storm surge, and tsunami. Flood risk is represented by the average risk to whole urban areas indicated from all causes of flooding. The sites of catastrophic floods in history are also shown on the map at the point of greatest impact. The role of flood defenses has been included in the risk analysis. Around the southern coast of the North Sea, flood defenses have had the greatest impact in reducing the flood risk that existed for centuries.

Risk Management Solutions (www.rms.com) is the world's leading provider of products and services for the quantification and management of natural hazard risks. Its clients include leading insurers, reinsurers, trading companies, and other financial institutions. Founded at Stanford University in 1988, RMS employs more than 600 people worldwide.

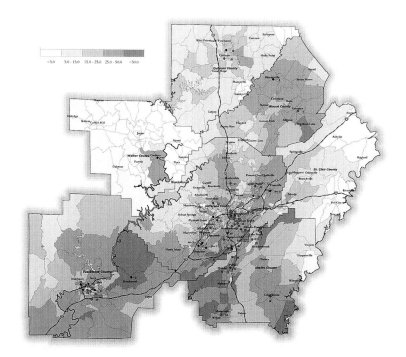

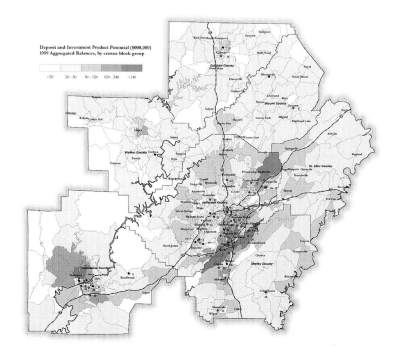

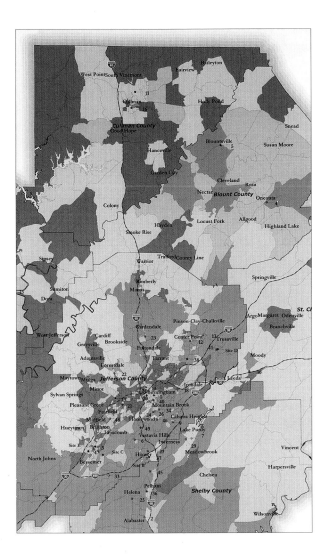

In 1999, Verdi and Company began a network study for a bank that included all of its locations within the Birmingham and Tuscaloosa, Alabama, area. This is a small portion of the bank's network, and the study was designed as a template for the rest of the network.

Recommendations for the network were formulated based on analysis of a combination of databases and identification of recent growth and development (residential and commercial). At the end of the study, Verdi and Company recommended closure, relocation, transformation, or status quo for various branches. Each branch on the map is color coded to these categories. Possible new sites for the relocations and new markets were also entered.

This map was used in the final presentation to the bank. The bank's representatives thought the map was useful because all the information they needed was on one large map. The map also contributed to the successful presentation because it served as visual representation of the written analysis and data.

Verdi and Company
Buffalo, New York

By Jeremy Kraft

Contact
Jeremy Kraft
jrkraft03@hotmail.com
Software
ArcView GIS 3.2
Hardware
Windows 98
Printer
HP DesignJet 750C+
Data Source(s)
Customer information file and Claritas
Map Type
Decision/Planning

Membership Analysis of the Long Beach Aquarium of the Pacific

Geo-Cart Systems
Long Beach, California

By Jim Woods

Contact

Jim Woods

jawoods-gcs@worldnet.att.net

Software

Atlas GIS™ DOS 2.1, Atlas GIS

Windows 4.0, and CellBNA

Hardware

PC Pentium 200

Printer

Epson Color Photo 1200

Data Source(s)

The Long Beach Aquarium of the

Pacific and various public and private

sources

Map Type

Decision/Planning

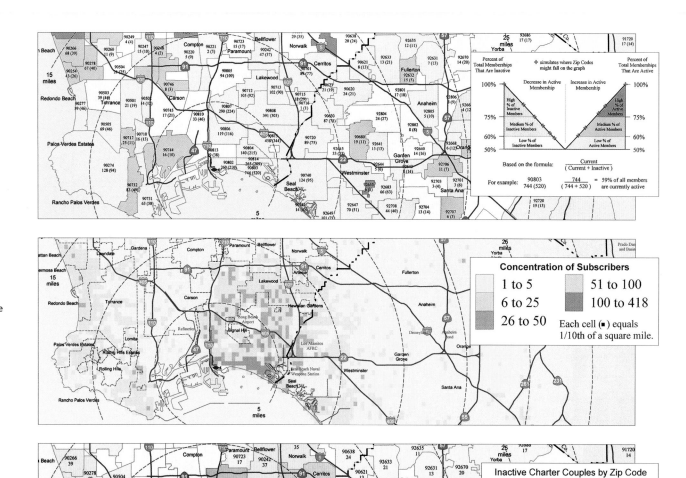

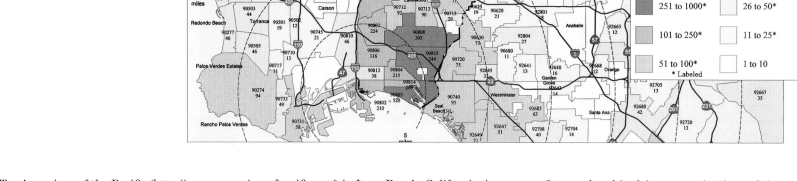

The Aquarium of the Pacific (http://www.aquariumofpacific.org/) in Long Beach, California, is a nonprofit, membership-driven organization, relying heavily on the support of its members. Within one year of opening, membership had risen to more than 53,000 households. To analyze and evaluate membership development and retention strategies, the Aquarium looked at the membership distribution from a geographic perspective. Atlas GIS DOS was used primarily for graphic manipulation of the base map data, while Atlas GIS Windows did geocoding and spatial analysis of the five major membership categories and map production. CellBNA created the spatial grid.

Thirty maps were produced for the atlas showing six different themes—spatial concentration and distribution of memberships, number of active members per membership class by ZIP Code, percent of active members per class by ZIP Code, number of inactive members per class by ZIP Code, percent of inactive members per class by ZIP Code, and level of active membership.

Three maps show the spatial concentration and distribution of memberships in which the richer color indicates more members. The level of active membership of dual (couples) charter subscribers map shows which ZIP Codes are predominantly retaining and which are predominantly losing members in that class.

Colliers International
Victoria, British Columbia, Canada

By Mike Shasko and
Nicole Ronald–Jones,
Clover Point Cartographics Ltd.

Contact
Mike Shasko
cloverpoint@pinc.com

Software
ArcInfo 7.2.1, ArcView GIS 3.1,
and CorelDraw

Printer
HP DesignJet 2500CP

Data Source(s)
Client hard-copy map and company
archived road line work

Map Type
Communication/Cartography

Developed for Colliers International, a global real estate services firm, this map shows all properties in the downtown core of Victoria, British Columbia, and includes streets and street names, cadastral lines, building footprints, the number of floors in a building, landmarks, and property type.

The initial work involved gathering base data and project specifications from Colliers. Each downtown property required an individually placed, unique label, and a TrueType font was developed to show the number of stories in a building. The font was created with CorelDraw and converted to a marker set in ArcView GIS. A proprietary symbol to mark one-way streets was also developed.

Downtown office, retail, warehouse, and parking spaces are usually not readily available in Victoria, and this map identifies all known properties in a clean, crisp presentation. Property managers use this map to identify available lease or sale properties to potential clients, and portions of the map can be enlarged for use in information brochures.

Apt	Apartment	⑦	Number of floors in building
B&B	Bed and Breakfast	P	Parking
C	Condominiums		Parkade area
O	Offices	PK - 100	Number of parking stalls
R	Retail		Park / Grass area
W	Warehouse / Showroom	CMN	One way street
V	Vacant		

Geomorphologic Map of Greece

Terra Ltd.
Athens, Greece

*By Thanos Doganis,
Apostolos Marnieros,
and Yannis Roukoutakis*

Contact
Thanos Doganis
thanos@terra.gr
Software
ArcInfo 7.1.2
Hardware
Compaq True 64 (Digital UNIX)
Printer
HP DesignJet 2500CP
Data Source(s)
Digital data (1:250,000) bathymetry
charts and Terra's digital data set
Map Type
Communication/Cartography

Although Terra Ltd.'s primary work is with data automation and the design of spatial databases, it published the Geomorphologic Map of Greece and the Geopolitical Map of Greece to assist teachers and students in their geography courses.

The land elevation tints for the geomorphologic map and the shaded relief were generated from a 100 by 100 meter digital elevation model. The elevation tints and the shaded relief for the bathymetry were derived from maps from the International Oceanographic Commission.

Shaded relief represents bathymetry because Greece is located at the boundaries of the Eurasian and African tectonic plates. This, along with the seismologic activity, produced an intense and characteristic shaded relief. The backdrops for both maps were produced using ARC GRID™ while the layout design was done with ARCPLOT™.

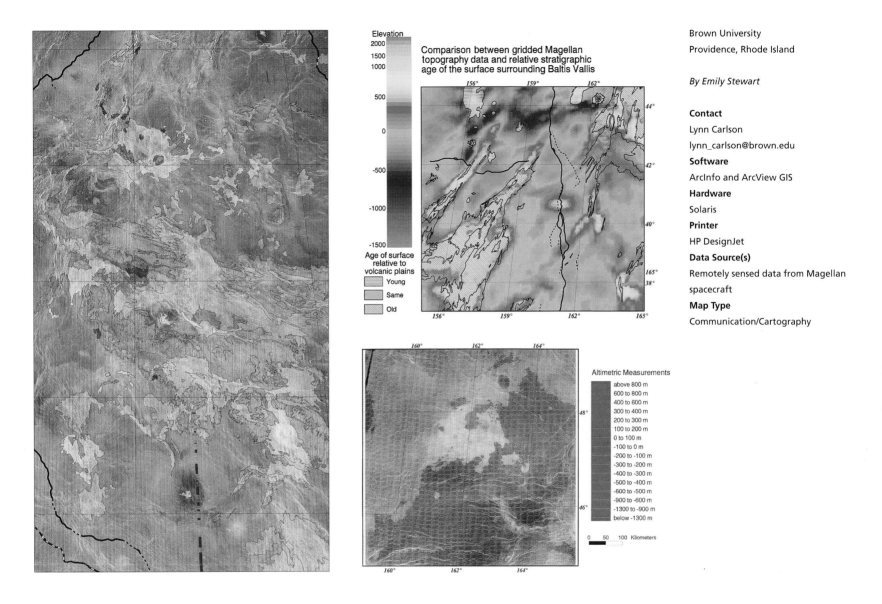

Comparison between gridded Magellan topography data and relative stratigraphic age of the surface surrounding Baltis Vallis

Elevation
2000
1500
1000
500
0
-500
-1000
-1500

Age of surface relative to volcanic plains
Young
Same
Old

Altimetric Measurements
above 800 m
600 to 800 m
400 to 600 m
300 to 400 m
200 to 300 m
100 to 200 m
0 to 100 m
-100 to 0 m
-200 to -100 m
-300 to -200 m
-400 to -300 m
-500 to -400 m
-600 to -500 m
-900 to -600 m
-1300 to -900 m
below -1300 m

0   50   100 Kilometers

Brown University
Providence, Rhode Island

By Emily Stewart

Contact
Lynn Carlson
lynn_carlson@brown.edu
Software
ArcInfo and ArcView GIS
Hardware
Solaris
Printer
HP DesignJet
Data Source(s)
Remotely sensed data from Magellan spacecraft
Map Type
Communication/Cartography

During the Magellan Mission to Venus in the 1990s, the Magellan satellite visited Venus and transmitted radar images and altimetric measurements from 97 percent of the planet. These images revealed that, like Earth, Venus has had an active geologic history modifying its surface by volcanism and tectonics. However, unlike Earth, Venus does not appear to be undergoing plate tectonics. This GIS relates the stratigraphic history to the tectonic and topographic history of a region and sheds some light on what forces drive tectonics on Venus.

Extending ArcView GIS for Mapping Planets

Because ArcView GIS was designed for use on Earth, some modifications were necessary to enable it to display Venus data properly. Peter Girard, formerly of ESRI–Boston, developed a Projection and Spheroid extension, which contains proper spheroid definitions for every large terrestrial body in the solar system. The Projection and Spheroid extension enables longitude to be measured positive west as it is on every planet except Venus and Earth and to range from 0 to 360 degrees instead of 180 to 180 degrees.

Geologic Map of the Baltis Vallis Region of Venus

Baltis Vallis is a canal, a sinuous channel one to three kilometers wide and more than 6,800 kilometers long that might have held lava. It is the longest known channel of any kind in the solar system, and it is formed entirely in a geologic unit mapped as plains with wrinkle ridges.

Comparing stratigraphic maps to topographic data of Baltis Vallis and other canals is useful for studying the relationships between stratigraphy and topography. A comparison between a map of the canals and gridded topography data reveals that the topography of the channel now undulates.

Beautiful Mount Jefferson

U.S. Department of the Interior,
Bureau of Land Management
Portland, Oregon

*By Jeffery S. Nighbert and
Shelley Moore*

Contact
Jeffery Nighbert
jnighber@or.blm.gov

Software
ArcInfo, ARCPLOT, ARC TIN™,
and ARC GRID
Hardware
Windows NT
Printer
ENCAD NovaJet 60
Data Source(s)
Ten-meter digital elevation models
Map Type
Communication/Cartography

This colorful display of Mount Jefferson in Oregon demonstrates new painted relief and three-dimensional surface viewing techniques using ARC Macro Language (AML™) programs for portraying landscapes in a combination map and perspective view format. The map presentation highlights the use of the new 10-meter digital elevation model data procured through a data sharing partnership with the U.S. Geological Survey by more than 15 different agencies including the Bureau of Land Management, U.S. Forest Service, Washington Department of Natural Resources, and the Oregon State Department of Forestry.

Used within the ARC GRID system, the painted relief AML programs can create wonderful cartographic products. This map provides further proof that ArcInfo can produce incredible views and cartographic products for presentation in a plot/poster format. These AMLs are available at the BLM Oregon State Office Web site www.or.blm.gov\gis.

The map authors also created this map to inspire other GIS users to learn to appreciate the beauty in the world around them and to put that inspiration into the maps they create.

The 1:25,000 map series was produced for more than 20 years by traditional cartographic methods. In 1996, the Department of Primary Industries, Water and Environment investigated automated methods of map production for the map series and decided that ArcInfo with a custom application was the best solution.

An application that uses ARCEDIT™ and ARCPLOT edits and plots map tiles with a minimum of input from users. The application enables users to place text, edit feature attributes, and change feature symbology while in the edit environment. With editing on the map tile complete, the automated plotting routines can generate a map composition. Map compositions are output for quality assurance using an HP DesignJet 5000PS, and then the map is color separated and output as PostScript files. The PostScript files are plotted on a Linotype-Hell 3030 as CMYK film plates for Cromalin proofing and final printing.

This method of map production has reduced compilation time for maps to about 25 percent of the time previously spent using traditional methods and has significantly reduced the costs. To date about 25 maps out of the 400 map series have been produced using these automated methods. The 1:25,000 series is nearing complete coverage of the state with significant revisions planned for the future.

The entire map series is viewable through the LIST Web site at www.thelist.tas.gov.au.

Department of Primary Industries, Water and Environment
Tasmania, Australia

By Bruce Graham and Max Neil

Contact
Stuart Fletcher
stuartf@dpiwe.tas.gov.au
Software
ArcInfo 7.2.1
Hardware
IBM RS/6000
Printer
HP DesignJet 5000PS and Linotype-Hell 3030
Data Source(s)
Department GIS database
Map Type
Automation

Official City Map for Spokane, Washington, 2000

City of Spokane
Spokane, Washington

By Bill Myers

Contact
Bill Myers
bmyers@spokanecity.org
Software
ArcInfo 7.2x
Hardware
Sun 450 server and Sun Ultra 1
workstation
Printer
HP DesignJet 755C
Data Source(s)
City of Spokane, Spokane County,
and U.S. Geological Survey
Map Type
Automation

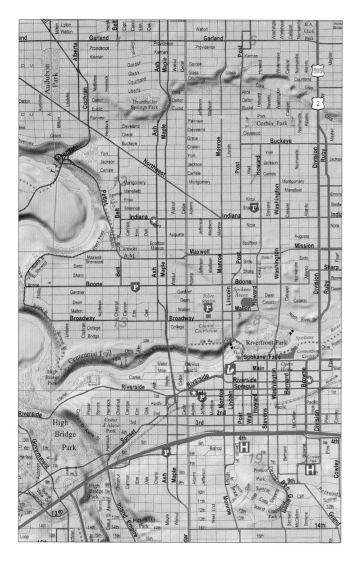

Replacing the city's traditional planimetric street map, the Spokane City Map was produced in ARCPLOT and ARC GRID using custom ARC Macro Language applications. The shaded relief backdrop is visually appealing and provides a regional geographic overview, while the automated production process enables GIS staff to easily generate updated maps.

This map was made possible by the availability of a variety of high-quality data sources. The city's planimetric base map data was derived from six-inch resolution orthophotography, and the shaded relief model was generated from U.S. Geological Survey 7.5-minute contours using the topogrid tools available in ArcInfo. This map is available for sale to the public.

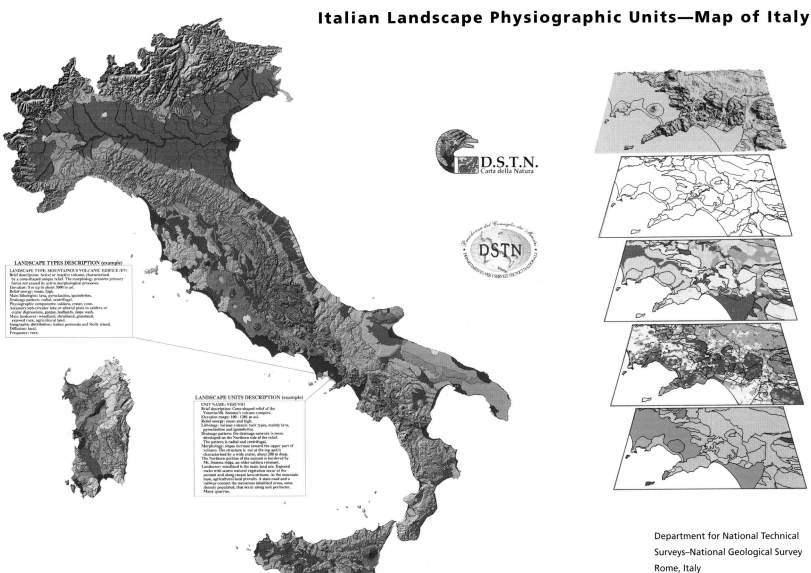

A 1:250,000-scale thematic map—the Italian Landscape Physiographic Units—defines homogeneous units within the landscape. The areas were identified by studying the composition and patterns of elements within each landscape.

Remote sensing techniques, mostly based on aerial photographs, field surveys, scientific literature, and regional studies, were used to do an integrated study of the composition and patterns of the physiographic elements of each landscape type. The landscape types and units and their descriptions were implemented in a GIS database. To identify the elements that define the landscape units at 1:250,000 scale, the information layer was compared to other thematic maps of the same area. A digital terrain model (DTM) as well as hydrography, lithology, and land cover maps were reviewed. In all, 37 landscape types and 2,053 landscape units for Italy were identified, mapped, described, and organized in a GIS.

Percent values of the total number of units were calculated as well as values for the area occupied by each landscape unit based on the total study area. The analysis of these values shows that some landscape types occur frequently, but their area is typically small. Conversely, some landscape types cover a wide area but do not occur as frequently. These statistics are important tools for the ongoing study of environmental quality and territorial vulnerability assessment of the landscape units of Italy.

Department for National Technical Surveys–National Geological Survey
Rome, Italy

By M. Amadei, R. Bagnaia, L. Laureti, D. Lavieri, F.R. Lugeri, N. Lugeri, and S. Nisio

Contact
Nicola Lugeri
nicola.lugeri@dstn.it
Software
ArcInfo 7.2
Hardware
DEC Alpha 255
Printer
OCE5200
Data Source(s)
Istituto Geografico Militare, Landsat Thematic Mapper, aerial photography, CORINE, and National Geological Survey of Italy
Map Type
Inventory

AAA Maps

AAA
Heathrow, Florida

By AAA Map Production Team

Contact
Miguel Garriga
mgarriga@national.aaa.com

Software
ArcInfo 7.2.1, ArcSDE™ 3.0.2,
Informix 9.2, and Maplex 3.3

Hardware
Sun Ultra Enterprise 4000
workstation

Printer
Lehigh Press

Data Source(s)
AAA, Navigation Technologies
Corporation, and Geographic
Data Technology

Map Type
Communication/Cartography

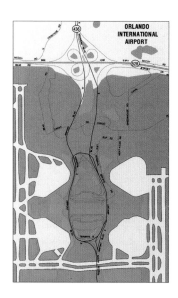

Orlando Vicinity Map

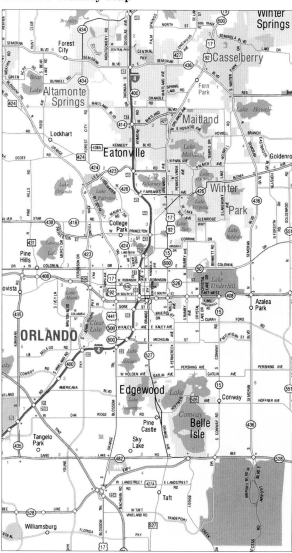

Metro Washington, D.C., CitiMap®

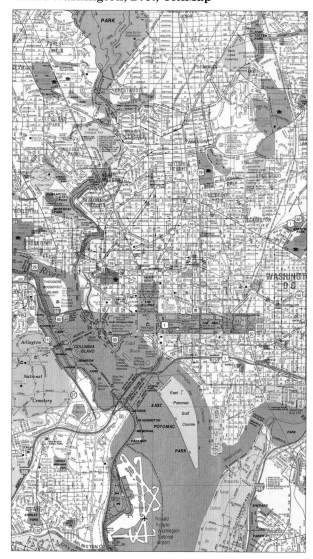

The Orlando Vicinity map and the Metro Washington, D.C., CitiMap® were derived from AAA's highly detailed nationwide ArcSDE database. All AAA GIS maps contain proprietary information supplied by AAA's Travel Information department and are designed to meet the touring needs of its members. GIS cartographers generalize the spatial data for each map product using rules for specific map types and scales. The Metro Washington, D.C., CitiMap provides detailed city-level coverage of the Washington, D.C., area including the beltway. The AAA Orlando Vicinity map illustrates the data presentation flexibility inherent with the scalable data within the AAA GIS database.

AAA has been producing quality maps since 1911. AAA GIS/Cartography incorporates traditional cartographic skills, automated production processes, and a multilayered GIS database to produce more than 44 million road maps annually for the association's 42 million members. The AAA GIS map production ArcSDE master database contains more than 50 GB of data and supports cartography and other electronic applications. Edits are made only in the master database, and cartographic edits are made to product-specific layers. Individual map views have custom projection parameters.

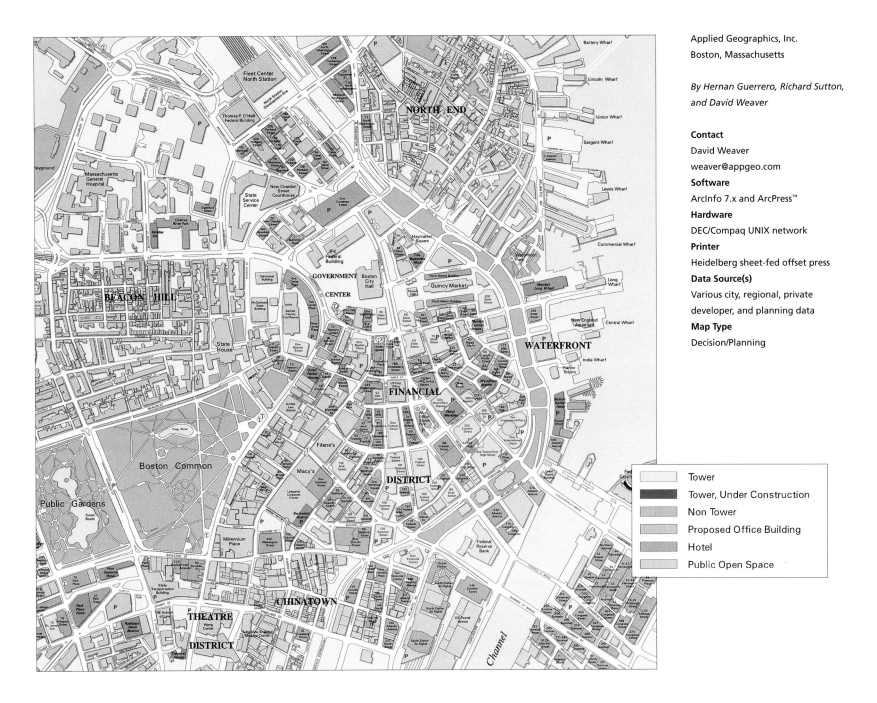

Downtown Boston

Applied Geographics, Inc.
Boston, Massachusetts

*By Hernan Guerrero, Richard Sutton,
and David Weaver*

Contact
David Weaver
weaver@appgeo.com
Software
ArcInfo 7.x and ArcPress™
Hardware
DEC/Compaq UNIX network
Printer
Heidelberg sheet-fed offset press
Data Source(s)
Various city, regional, private
developer, and planning data
Map Type
Decision/Planning

Applied Geographics, Inc., produced and maintains this up-to-date base map of downtown Boston, which is used for various GIS and publishing projects. This edition of the map highlights buildings for a real estate developer and depicts the most recent development and planning for this historic city.

The Seaport District, built on landfill, is undergoing extensive development, and the center of downtown Boston has shifted toward this district. In addition, the "Big Dig," shown as a corridor of green space, is reshaping a corridor extending through the Financial District, Waterfront, and the North End. The Boston Convention Center and the Fan Pier, although not yet built, are also shown in this map, which represents an interesting blended view of Boston in its existing and planned condition.

Sun-Illuminated Seafloor Topography and Backscatter Intensity of Stellwagen Bank National Marine Sanctuary

 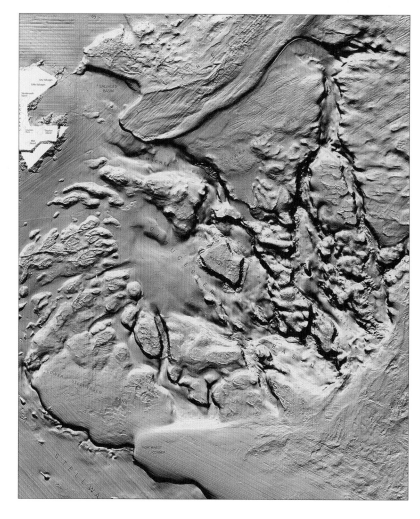

U.S. Geological Survey
Woods Hole, Massachusetts

*By Jessica L. Baker, Tanya S. Unger,
and Page C. Valentine*

Contact
Page Valentine
pvalentine@usgs.gov
Software
ArcInfo and ArcView GIS
Hardware
UNIX
Printer
HP DesignJet
Data Source(s)
U.S. Geological Survey
Map Type
Communication/Cartography

This is part of a map series about the Stellwagen Bank National Marine Sanctuary region. The maps are products of a 1994–96 survey that used a multibeam echo sounder to map 1,100-square-nautical miles of the seafloor and show new seafloor topography, sun-illuminated (shaded relief) seafloor topographic imagery, and sun-illuminated topography combined with the backscatter intensity of the seafloor. Backscatter intensity is a measure of the hardness and roughness of the seafloor as determined from the strength of sound waves reflected from the seabed during the survey.

Unnatural-looking stripes and patterns parallel or perpendicular to survey track lines are artifacts of data collection. Blank areas represent places where no data exists. Major topographic features depicted in the maps were formed by glacial processes, and in broad terms, these features are interpreted to represent a geologic history that developed in several stages. The sea invaded the region formerly occupied by ice, and glacial features were partly eroded forming some new deposits. Today, the seafloor is modified mainly by strong southwestward flowing bottom currents caused by storm winds from the northeast. These currents erode sediments from the shallow banks and transport them into the basins. With time, the banks become coarser as sand and mud are removed and gravel remains. The western flanks of the banks as well as adjacent basins are built up by deposits of mud and sand.

The Stellwagen Bank National Marine Sanctuary Mapping Project is a cooperative effort of the U.S. Geological Survey and the National Oceanic and Atmospheric Administration with support from the University of New Brunswick and the Canadian Hydrographic Service.

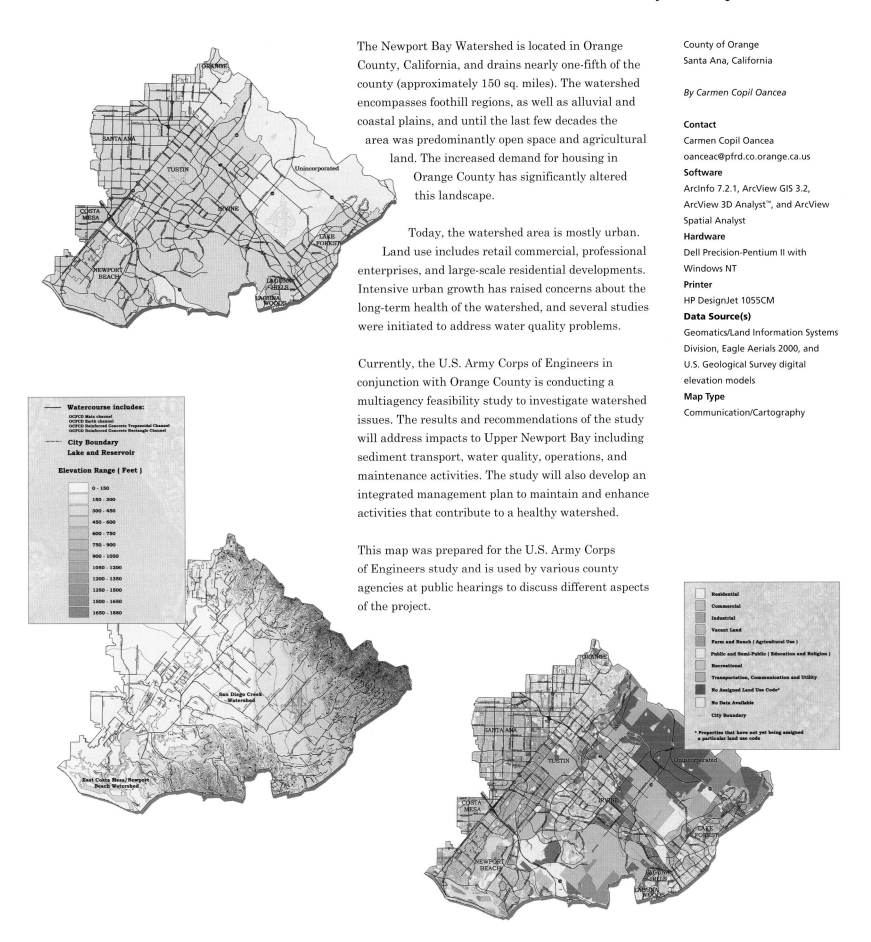

The Newport Bay Watershed is located in Orange County, California, and drains nearly one-fifth of the county (approximately 150 sq. miles). The watershed encompasses foothill regions, as well as alluvial and coastal plains, and until the last few decades the area was predominantly open space and agricultural land. The increased demand for housing in Orange County has significantly altered this landscape.

Today, the watershed area is mostly urban. Land use includes retail commercial, professional enterprises, and large-scale residential developments. Intensive urban growth has raised concerns about the long-term health of the watershed, and several studies were initiated to address water quality problems.

Currently, the U.S. Army Corps of Engineers in conjunction with Orange County is conducting a multiagency feasibility study to investigate watershed issues. The results and recommendations of the study will address impacts to Upper Newport Bay including sediment transport, water quality, operations, and maintenance activities. The study will also develop an integrated management plan to maintain and enhance activities that contribute to a healthy watershed.

This map was prepared for the U.S. Army Corps of Engineers study and is used by various county agencies at public hearings to discuss different aspects of the project.

County of Orange
Santa Ana, California

By Carmen Copil Oancea

Contact
Carmen Copil Oancea
oanceac@pfrd.co.orange.ca.us

Software
ArcInfo 7.2.1, ArcView GIS 3.2, ArcView 3D Analyst™, and ArcView Spatial Analyst

Hardware
Dell Precision-Pentium II with Windows NT

Printer
HP DesignJet 1055CM

Data Source(s)
Geomatics/Land Information Systems Division, Eagle Aerials 2000, and U.S. Geological Survey digital elevation models

Map Type
Communication/Cartography

Public Internet Mapping

Sphere of Influence Maps

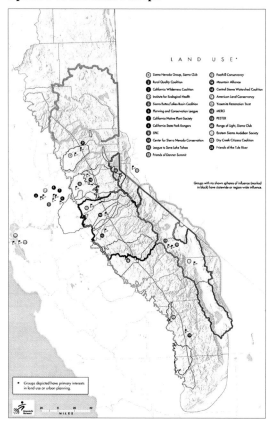

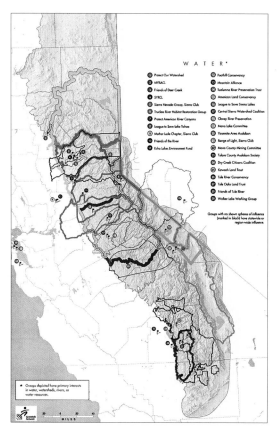

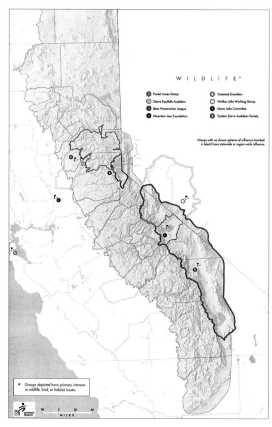

GreenInfo Network
San Francisco, California

By Brian Cohen, Aubrey Dugger, and Louis Jaffe

Contact
Larry Orman
larry@greeninfo.org
Software
ArcView GIS 3.2
Printer
HP LaserJet 8500DN
Data Source(s)
U.S. Geological Survey, U.S. Census
Bureau TIGER files, and client data
Map Type
Communication/Cartography

GreenInfo Network developed the Sphere of Influence map series (above) to help a coalition of 60 conservation nonprofits in the Sierra Nevada understand where they share common issues and which issues are not being addressed by current efforts. The map shows 15 issue areas, and the polygons represent each group's "turf" for an issue area. The large number of groups required developing extensive display techniques of line weight and color to distinguish each group from the other.

Greenbelt Alliance's At-Risk map (right) shows lands in the path of suburban sprawl in the California Bay Area. Careful attention to map colors was required for the greatest viewer impact. Shaded relief was downsampled to avoid visual noise and emphasize basic patterns. There are more GreenInfo maps online at www.greeninfo.org.

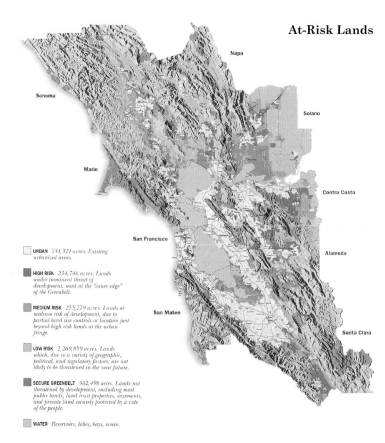

At-Risk Lands

URBAN *741,321 acres. Existing urbanized areas.*

HIGH RISK *234,746 acres. Lands under imminent threat of development, most at the "inner edge" of the Greenbelt.*

MEDIUM RISK *253,779 acres. Lands at medium risk of development, due to partial land use controls or location just beyond high risk lands at the urban fringe.*

LOW RISK *2,269,859 acres. Lands which, due to a variety of geographic, political, and regulatory factors, are not likely to be threatened in the near future.*

SECURE GREENBELT *982,498 acres. Lands not threatened by development, including most public lands, land trust properties, easements, and private land securely protected by a vote of the people.*

WATER *Reservoirs, lakes, bays, ocean.*

Railroads of the Civil War—Confederate and Union Movements in the Chickamauga/Chattanooga Campaigns

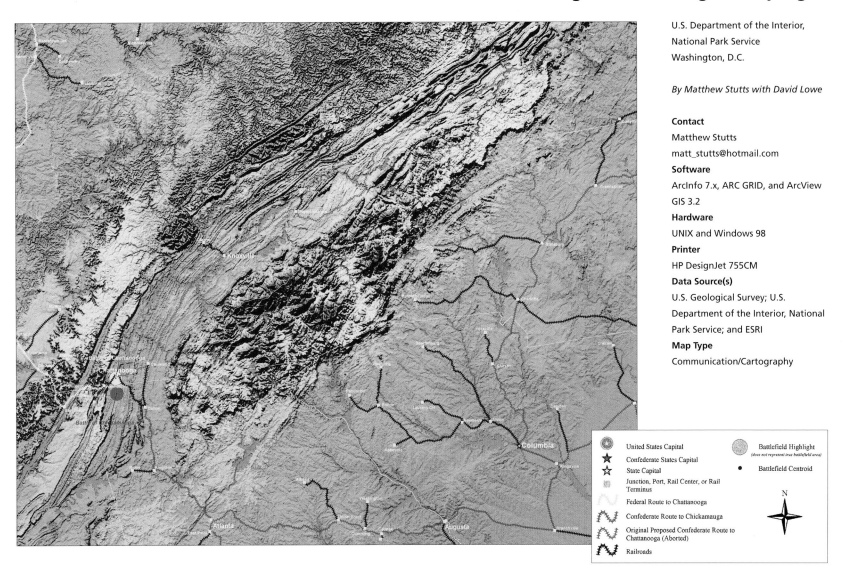

U.S. Department of the Interior,
National Park Service
Washington, D.C.

By Matthew Stutts with David Lowe

Contact
Matthew Stutts
matt_stutts@hotmail.com
Software
ArcInfo 7.x, ARC GRID, and ArcView
GIS 3.2
Hardware
UNIX and Windows 98
Printer
HP DesignJet 755CM
Data Source(s)
U.S. Geological Survey; U.S.
Department of the Interior, National
Park Service; and ESRI
Map Type
Communication/Cartography

This map was part of a series of maps used for updating the appendices of the Civil War Sites Advisory Commission Report on the Nation's Civil War Battlefields. A map detailing the routes taken by the Federal and Confederate troops toward the battles at Chickamauga and Chattanooga was not a necessary addition to the appendices, but rather it developed out of the authors' interest.

The American Civil War saw the first large-scale use of rail transport in modern warfare. From the onset of the war in 1861, both Federal and Confederate strategists realized the importance of troop and supply mobility via rail. The Union states enjoyed distinct rail superiority, and four northern states alone had greater than 22 percent of the miles of track in the entire south.

Most of the tracks in the north were constructed of a similar gauge. Confederate rails were of various incompatible gauges that served primarily to carry cotton and other crops to coast or river ports. Freight often had to be offloaded and moved across a town on wagons to a competing rail depot served by a different gauge track. These inefficiencies limited the speed or distance the Confederacy could transfer troops and supplies to a threatened point.

After 1862, Federals began to penetrate deep into southern territory intent on breaking up the railroads or rebuilding them to transport their own troops and supplies. The south fell further behind. The Confederacy transferred troops from Virginia to Georgia to fight at Chickamauga in September 1863, and the Union responded within weeks with a rail movement of its own from Virginia to Tennessee. These were among the largest troop movements by rail during the Civil War and offer a revealing comparison of the relative advantages of the north versus south.

Middle Rio Grande Conservancy District—The Ribbon of Green

Middle Rio Grande Conservancy
District
Albuquerque, New Mexico

*By Fred Bertola, Mike Montano,
DeAnna Rands, and Douglas Strech*

Contact
Douglas Strech
dstrech@mrgcd.dst.nm.us

Software
ArcInfo 7.2.1 and ArcView GIS 3.2

Hardware
Windows NT

Printer
HP DesignJet 755CM

Data Source(s)
ArcInfo coverages, shapefiles, and
ERDAS IMAGINE files

Map Type
Inventory

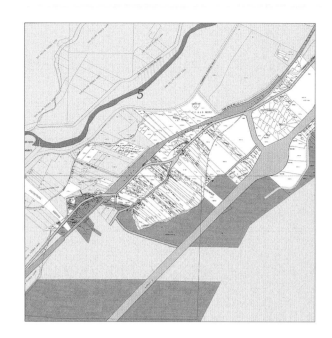

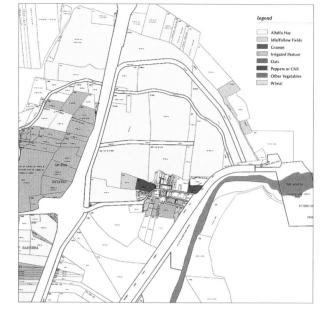

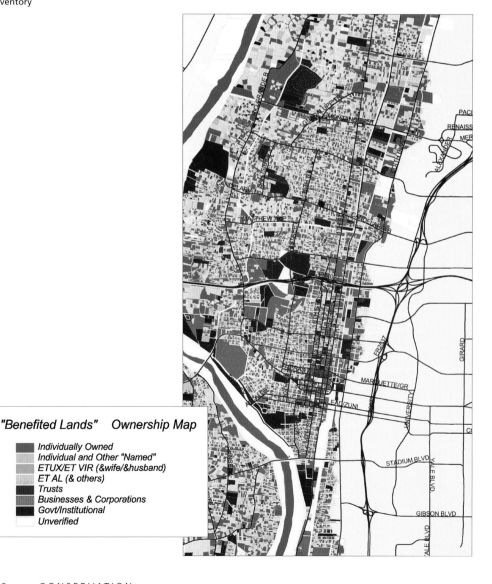

"Benefited Lands" Ownership Map

- Individually Owned
- Individual and Other "Named"
- ETUX/ET VIR (&wife/&husband)
- ET AL (& others)
- Trusts
- Businesses & Corporations
- Govt/Institutional
- Unverified

The green ribbon of life that stretches from Cochiti
Lake to the northern boundary of Bosque del Apache
National Wildlife Refuge is the only land use pattern
for hundreds of miles along the Rio Grande River.
That green Middle Valley exists because of the Middle
Rio Grande Conservancy District (MRGCD).

The MRGCD is a political subdivision of the state of
New Mexico that is governed by an elected board of
directors. The MRGCD is in the process of identifying
and verifying all property that lies within its benefited
lands. All real property owners within the benefited
lands are eligible to vote. Qualification to vote in the
MRGCD election is based solely on property ownership and not by voter registration. The MRGCD is
working closely with the assessor's office of the four
counties (Sandoval, Bernalillo, Valencia, and Socorro)
to complete its database of all real property within
its boundaries.

The district encompasses approximately 150 river
miles, and it varies from one to five miles in width.
The total area is 277,760 acres with 28,500 acres
of Indian land and 128,787 acres of irrigable lands.
Approximately 60,000 acres use irrigation water.

Footprints on Federal Lands—GIS Modeling of Human Use of Public Lands

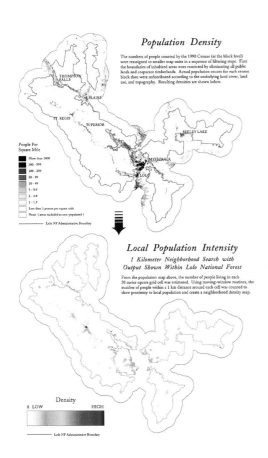

Population Density

The numbers of people counted by the 1990 Census (at the block level) were reassigned to smaller map units in a sequence of filtering steps. First the boundaries of inhabited areas were restricted by eliminating all public lands and corporate timberlands. Actual population counts for each census block then were redistributed according to the underlying land cover, land use, and topography. Resulting densities are shown below.

People Per
Square Mile

More than 1000
300 - 999
100 - 299
50 - 99
10 - 49
5 - 9.9
3 - 4.9
1 - 2.9
Less than 1 person per square mile
None (areas excluded as non-populated)

——— Lolo NF Administrative Boundary

Local Population Intensity
1 Kilometer Neighborhood Search with Output Shown Within Lolo National Forest

From the population map above, the number of people living in each 30 meter square grid cell was estimated. Using moving-window routines, the number of people within a 1 km distance around each cell was counted to show proximity to local population and create a neighborhood density map.

Density
0 LOW   HIGH

——— Lolo NF Administrative Boundary

Roads & Trails

Roads and trails provide an estimate of an area's accessibility to people. They also may have physical impacts on an ecosystem, such as increased sedimentation. Data were acquired from the U.S. Forest Service.

Improved Roads

Unimproved Roads

Trails

Road & Trail Density
1 Kilometer Neighborhood Search with Output Shown Within Lolo National Forest

Output model has been weighted by factors of 3 - 2 - 1 for "Improved Roads" - "Unimproved Roads" - "Trails", respectively.

Density
0 LOW   HIGH

——— Lolo NF Administrative Boundary

Large areas in western North America are publicly owned and managed by government agencies for a variety of uses. As the human population continues to grow, competing interests will place mounting pressures on how resources from these lands should be managed and used by people.

This poster illustrates a GIS protocol for modeling the intensity of local human use of public lands. It focuses on a 2.2 million hectare area surrounding the Lolo National Forest in western Montana.

The method offers land managers and planners a way to evaluate and visualize human impacts in a spatial sense. For instance, the dasymetric map of human population density provides a more detailed picture of where people live than does a traditional choropleth map of census data.

By incorporating the network of roads and trails, areas that are readily accessible to humans—and hence more likely to be used—can be identified. Although this method is suited to an assessment of human impacts on terrestrial and aquatic species, it could be applied to problems in other disciplines, and in particular, to risk assessments related to wildfire or exposure to contaminants.

Further details are available as written by Schumacher, J.V., R.L. Redmond, M.M. Hart, and M.E. Jensen in "Mapping Patterns of Human Use and Potential Resource Conflicts on Public Lands," *Environmental Monitoring and Assessment* 64:127–137, 2000.

Wildlife Spatial Analysis Lab, Montana Cooperative Wildlife Research Unit
Missoula, Montana

By Melissa M. Hart, Mark E. Jensen, Roland L. Redmond, and James V. Schumacher

Contact
Jim Schumacher
jim@wru.umt.edu

Software
ArcInfo 7.1, ARCPLOT, and ARC GRID
Hardware
IBM RS/6000
Printer
Raster Graphic 436
Data Source(s)
1990 U.S. Census block data, predicted distributions of terrestrial vertebrates from the Montana Gap Analysis, predicted bull trout distributions from the Interior Columbia Basin Ecosystem Management Project, roads and trails from the U.S. Forest Service cartographic feature files, and U.S. Geological Survey hydrographic data
Map Type
Modeling/Analytical

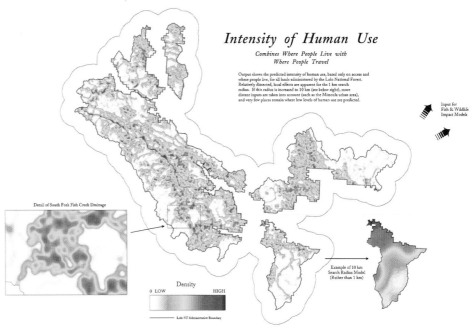

Intensity of Human Use
Combines Where People Live with Where People Travel

Output shows the predicted intensity of human use, based only on access and where people live, for all lands administered by the Lolo National Forest. Relatively dissected, local effects are apparent for the 1 km search radius. If this radius is increased to 10 km (see below right), more distant inputs are taken into account (such as the Missoula urban area), and very few places remain where low levels of human use are predicted.

Input for
Fish & Wildlife
Impact Models

Detail of South Fork Fish Creek Drainage

Density
0 LOW   HIGH

——— Lolo NF Administrative Boundary

Example of 10 km
Search Radius Model
(Rather than 1 km)

Ecosystems of the Eastern Andes Mountain Range in Colombia

Alexander von Humboldt Biological
Research Institute
Villa de Leyva, Colombia

*By Dolors Armenteras, Carol Franco,
and Hector Villarreal*

Contact
Dolors Armenteras
darmenteras@humboldt.org.co

Software
ArcView GIS 3.1 and ERDAS
IMAGINE 8.3
Hardware
Dell Workstation 400
Printer
HP DesignJet 755CM
Data Source(s)
Landsat Thematic Mapper and
cartography
Map Type
Communication/Cartography and
Decision/Planning

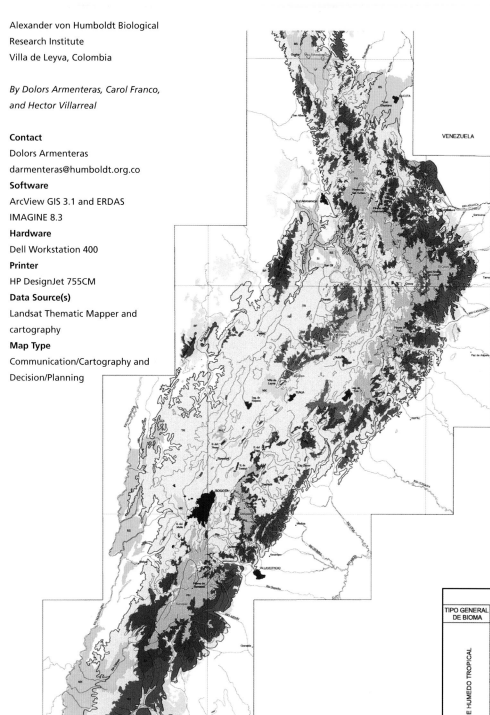

This map displays 13 types of ecosystems in the Colombian Eastern Andes as interpreted from Landsat Thematic Mapper satellite images covering this area.

Producing the map was part of an Andean ecoregional project, which identified priority areas for conservation in the Colombian Eastern Andes forests. Specifically, the project analyzed the distribution and fragmented state of the Andean ecosystems in the region and tried to identify which ecosystems were inadequately represented in the current network of protected areas. The project also delineated sites for establishing future conservation areas.

The biodiversity of the Andes is particularly vulnerable to loss from human disturbance. More than half (51 percent) of the ecosystems studied were altered because of this. This is the first Colombian Eastern Andes map of natural ecosystems at this level of resolution.

This research was developed with support from The Nature Conservancy, Fundación Natura, and the ESRI conservation program.

LEYENDA				
TIPO GENERAL DE BIOMA	BIOMAS	ECOSISTEMAS	SIMBOLO	SUPERFICIE ACTUAL (ha) (2)
ZONOBIOMA DEL BOSQUE HÚMEDO TROPICAL	Orobiomas Andinos	Bosques Secos y matorrales secundarios xerofíticos de valles intramontanos (<~ 1200 m) (1)	BS	377.475
		Matorrales Xerofíticos de enclaves sub-andinos y andinos (>~ 1200m) (1)	MX	128.700
		Bosques Sub-andinos (1000-2000m)	BU	1'796.250
		Bosques Andinos (2000- ~3000m)		1'567.525
		Páramos Húmedos	PH	920.875
		Páramos Secos	PS	60.275
		Superpáramo	SP	20.925
		Nival	NV	3.775
	Pedobiomas Andinos	Bosques Sub-andinos de Roble	BR	128.350
		Sabanas Intra-andinas (< ~ 1200m)	SI	29.950
	Helobiomas Andinos	Humedales	HM	16.800
	Bosques Tropicales del Magdalena Medio, la Orinoquia y la Amazonia	Bosques de planicies sedimentarias (3)	BP	——
		TOTAL ECOSISTEMAS NATURALES		5'050.900
		Ecosistemas Transformados	TR	5'269.475
		TOTAL ECOSISTEMAS TRANSFORMADOS		5'269.475
		TOTAL		10'320.375

(1) Ecosistemas con alto nivel de degradación   (2) Mayor de 1000 m de elevación   (3) Ecosistema no considerado en el estudio

Habitat Quality for San Joaquin Kit Fox on Managed and Private Lands

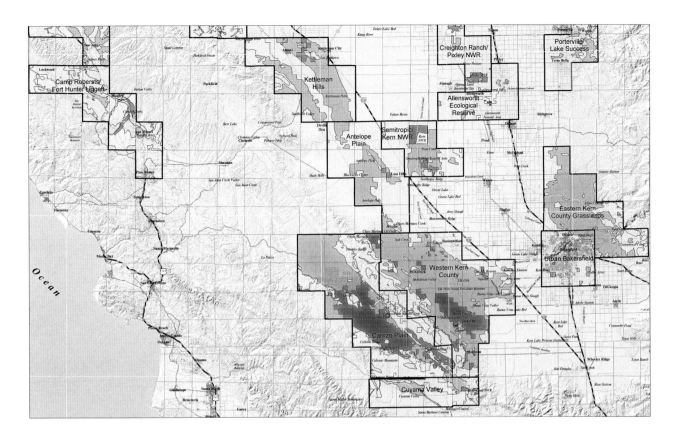

California State University, Sacramento (CSUS)/Endangered Species Recovery Program (ESRP) Fresno, California

By Patrick A. Kelly, Scott E. Phillips, and Daniel F. Williams

Contact
Scott Phillips
gis@esrp.csustan.edu
Software
ArcView GIS
Hardware
Generic x86
Plotter
HP DesignJet 650C
Data Source(s)
University of California, Santa Barbara (UCSB) Gap Analysis; U.S. Geological Survey; California Department of Forestry; U.S. Bureau of Reclamation; U.S. Bureau of Transportation Statistics; and U.S. Bureau of the Census
Map Type
Inventory

Recovery actions for the federally listed San Joaquin kit fox are considered critical to the recovery of threatened and endangered upland species of the San Joaquin Valley of California. Kit fox recovery actions will provide an umbrella of protection for San Joaquin Valley ecosystems and many of those species that require less habitat.

The Endangered Species Recovery Program (ESRP) is conducting a study to estimate the quality of habitat under managed/protected lands and under private ownership. Kit fox populations were delineated from public land survey townships that corresponded to the general area of the named population. The three core kit fox populations were assigned 16 townships each, eight secondary populations were assigned eight townships each, and eight tertiary populations were assigned four townships each.

Within each population unit, habitat quality was assigned to three categories—best, fair, and unsuitable—based on the percentage of appropriate land cover and the ruggedness of terrain. Lands with 90 percent or more of annual grassland or scrub vegetation and with slopes of less than 5 percent were considered the best habitat for the kit fox. Lands with between 5 and 10 percent slopes and more than 50 percent annual grassland or scrubland cover were considered fair habitat excluding the lands classified as the best habitat. The remaining lands were classified as unsuitable habitat.

An identity overlay was done on the habitat class data to classify each category by the management status of the land area. The resulting data consists of six categories of land status and habitat quality. The area and percentages of each category will be used in modeling efforts for alternative farmland retirement strategies for restoring San Joaquin Valley ecosystems.

Mapping External Threats

U.S. Department of the Interior,
National Park Service
Twentynine Palms, California

By Hassan Basagic

Contact
Hassan Basagic
hassan_basagic@nps.gov

Software
ArcView GIS 3.2

Data Source(s)
U.S. Geological Survey 30-meter
digital elevation models and Joshua
Tree National Park resource data

Map Type
Communication/Cartography,
Decision/Planning, and Inventory

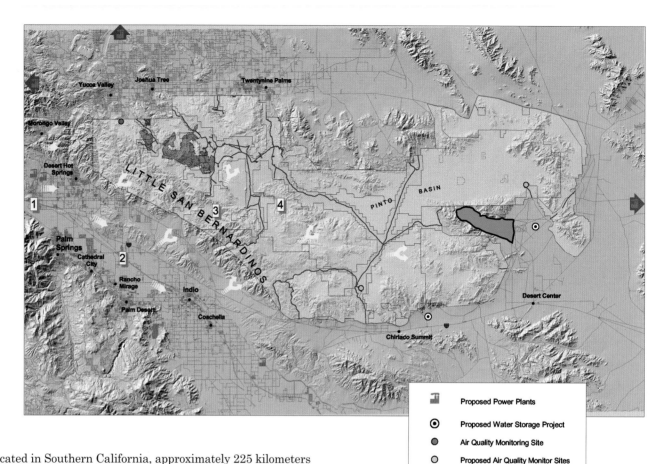

Legend:
- Proposed Power Plants
- Proposed Water Storage Project
- Air Quality Monitoring Site
- Proposed Air Quality Monitor Sites
- 1999 Juniper Fire Complex
- Eagle Mountain Landfill
- Park Roads
- Roads
- Wilderness Areas
- Park Boundary

Joshua Tree National Park is located in Southern California, approximately 225 kilometers east of Los Angeles and spans the transition between the Mojave and the Colorado deserts. It provides the unique habitat that Joshua trees require and contains some of the most interesting rock formations found in the California desert.

The park is a distinctive landscape and a valuable biological resource. Often political boundaries cannot provide full protection against external activities, which can negatively affect the area. This map identifies the major threats to Joshua Tree National Park, which include a proposed landfill along the park border, invasive introduced wildlife and vegetation species, urbanization of the communities surrounding the park, and high impact recreation within the park.

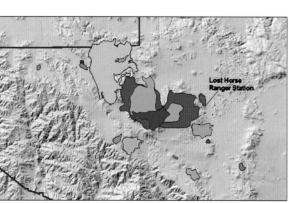

Fires over One Acre from 1967–1998

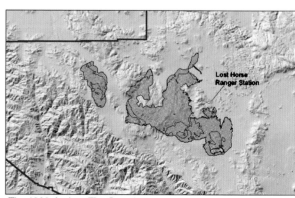

The 1999 Juniper Fire Complex

Relocating a Military Flight Training Route over Joshua Tree National Park

U.S. Department of the Interior,
National Park Service
Twentynine Palms, California

By Gary Lindberg

Contact
Gary Lindberg
gary_lindberg@nps.gov
Software
ArcInfo 7.2.1 and ArcView GIS 3.2
Hardware
Sun SPARC 20 workstation and
Micron Millennia Pro Plus
Printer
HP DesignJet 755CM
Data Source(s)
U.S. Geological Survey 30-meter
digital elevation models and Joshua
Tree National Park resource data
images of military aircraft
downloaded from U.S. Navy and U.S.
Marine Web sites
Map Type
Communication/Cartography,
Decision/Planning, and Inventory

Legend:
- Existing Training Route
- Proposed Training Route
- Training Route Corridors
- Tortoise Location
- Wilderness
- Non-Wilderness
- Park Boundary
- Roads
- Observation Point
- Campground
- Picnic Area
- Visitor Center
- Historic Site

In 1999, the National Park Service contacted the U.S. Department of the Navy about exploring the possibility of moving VR-1257, a training flight route crossing the park. The cooperative efforts of the U.S. Navy, U.S. Air Force, and Joshua Tree National Park personnel succeeded in moving a section of VR-1257 to a more remote portion of the park while still providing pilots required training opportunities.

Park personnel provided the GIS analysis and mapping for the environmental analysis report. This map is from that report, and along with several other maps, it was part of a display by the ESRI Conservation Program, which supports Joshua Tree National Park with its GIS efforts.

GIS analysis showed that the original 4 nautical mile wide corridor flies over 12 of the 15 historic sites and 7 of the 9 campgrounds in the park. Moving the training route to the south edge of the park reduced this to two historic sites and no campgrounds.

The maps shown here are images of maps actually used in the environmental assessment for the modification of VR-1257. Black and white maps were used whenever possible to reduce printing costs.

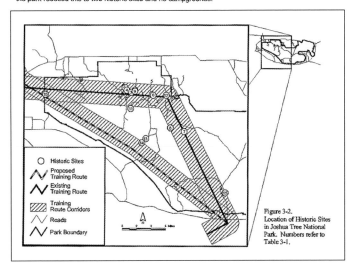

Figure 3-2.
Location of Historic Sites
in Joshua Tree National
Park. Numbers refer to
Table 3-1.

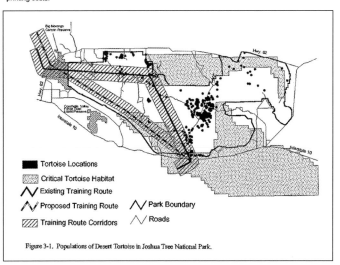

Figure 3-1. Populations of Desert Tortoise in Joshua Tree National Park.

Global Major Habitat Types and Natural World Heritage Sites

The Nature Conservancy,
International Conservation Science
Arlington, Virginia

*By Roger Sayre and
Leonardo Sotomayor*

Contact
Leonardo Sotomayor
lsotomayor@tnc.org

Software
ArcView GIS 3.2 and Adobe
Illustrator
Hardware
Windows NT
Printer
HP DesignJet 1055CM
Data Source(s)
World Wildlife Fund, World Bank,
and World Conservation and
Monitoring Centre
Map Type
Decision/Planning

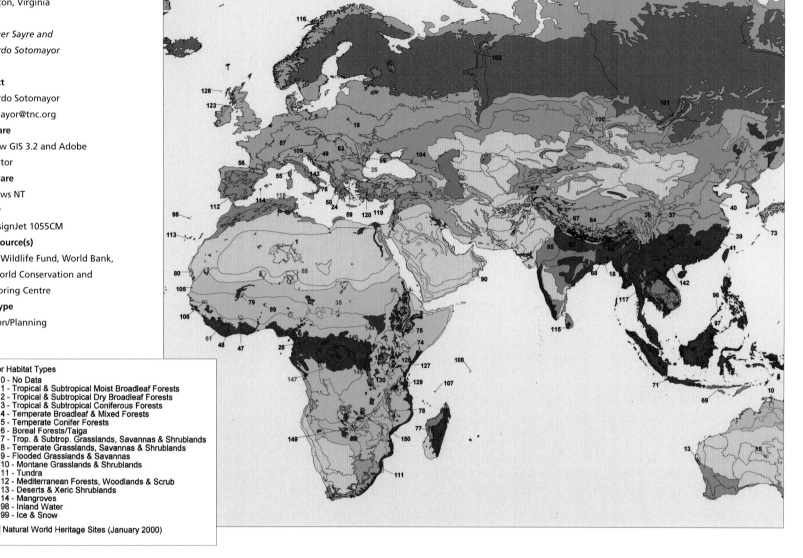

Major Habitat Types
- 0 - No Data
- 1 - Tropical & Subtropical Moist Broadleaf Forests
- 2 - Tropical & Subtropical Dry Broadleaf Forests
- 3 - Tropical & Subtropical Coniferous Forests
- 4 - Temperate Broadleaf & Mixed Forests
- 5 - Temperate Conifer Forests
- 6 - Boreal Forests/Taiga
- 7 - Trop. & Subtrop. Grasslands, Savannas & Shrublands
- 8 - Temperate Grasslands, Savannas & Shrublands
- 9 - Flooded Grasslands & Savannas
- 10 - Montane Grasslands & Shrublands
- 11 - Tundra
- 12 - Mediterranean Forests, Woodlands & Scrub
- 13 - Deserts & Xeric Shrublands
- 14 - Mangroves
- 98 - Inland Water
- 99 - Ice & Snow

Natural World Heritage Sites (January 2000)

The United Nations Educational, Scientific, and Cultural Organization (UNESCO) International Union for the Conservation of Nature (IUCN) World Heritage site network affords protection to the world's major habitat types (MHTs). Staff from The Nature Conservancy's International Conservation Science Department undertook a global-scale conservation gap analysis to determine UNESCO/IUCN's level of protection.

World Heritage sites were overlaid on MHTs, and the overall protection (area and percent) of each MHT by World Heritage site was calculated. MHTs are broad areas with similar climates that comprise similar ecoregions as defined by the World Wildlife Fund and the World Bank.

Natural World Heritage sites (NWHS) were obtained from the World Conservation Monitoring Centre in 1998. This GIS layer was then corrected and updated by The Nature Conservancy to include new sites for 1999 and any changes in site status. The NWHS GIS layer consists of 150 sites and respective polygon(s) delimiting the protected areas' boundaries including sites considered to be in danger.

This map shows that the relative protection of sites was quite variable. For example, mangroves were relatively well protected at 4.7 percent of their total area. Tropical and subtropical dry broadleaf forests, however, show minimal protection by World Heritage sites at 0.1 percent of the total area protected. The map and analysis are useful in considering placement of future World Heritage sites, especially if representation of all MHTs is a goal of the World Heritage sites network.

Vegetation Succession

Vegetation Zones

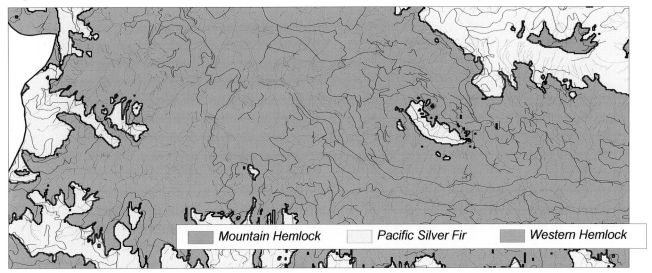

Mountain Hemlock Pacific Silver Fir Western Hemlock

Year 40 Vegetation (without harvest)

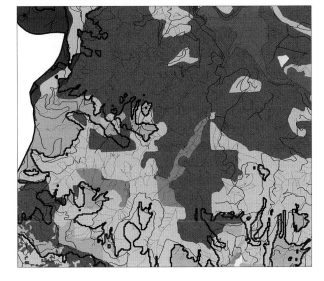

Current Vegetation

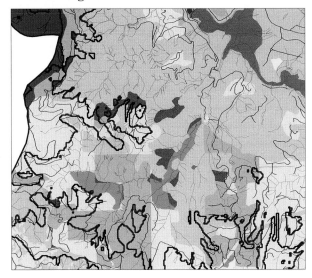

Foster Wheeler Environmental
Bothell, Washington

By Mary Jo Kochel

Contact
Mary Jo Kochel
mkochel@fwenc.com
Software
ArcView GIS 3.1
Hardware
Windows NT
Printer
HP DesignJet 1055
Data Source(s)
U.S. Department of Agriculture, U.S. Geological Survey, and private timber companies
Map Type
Modeling/Analytical

A spatial GIS model of landscape changes in vegetation cover (habitat types) over time for a land exchange project shows predictions under different alternatives. These predictions were necessary to assess effects on wildlife over the short term, long term, and extended long term. The vegetation succession and harvest model is useful as a descriptive tool, depicting broad habitat patterns across the landscape rather than predicting conditions at a particular place or in a particular year.

Model predictions are most accurate for the long term and extended long term as the purpose and need of the land exchange is primarily tied to the long term and extended long term. Short-term predictions (i.e., predictions of 10 years or less) are sensitive to assumptions made about harvest patterns. In the absence of site-specific timber harvest plans, short-term predictions about which stands to harvest are approximate. Long-term and extended long-term predictions have low sensitivity to harvest assumptions but are more sensitive to assumptions made regarding succession. Changes in succession assumptions are slow to take effect while changes in harvest assumptions take effect rapidly.

The model is polygon-based, and the polygons are defined based on habitat types, ownership boundaries, and section lines. Each polygon can either stay the same, be harvested, or change to the next older type in the successional chain during each period. The time period is 10 years.

Succession is modeled using a set of lookup tables, which are specific to each vegetation series. Each lookup table defines the length of time a polygon spends in each habitat type given its series.

Managing the Spread of the Asian Longhorned Beetle

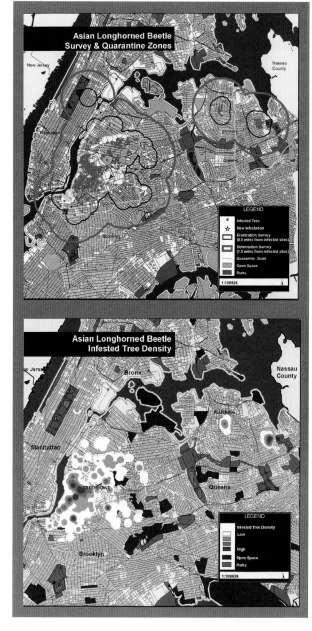

City of New York Parks and
Recreation
New York, New York

By Micaela Birmingham

Contact
Paul Katzer
paul.katzer@parks.nyc.gov
Software
ArcView GIS
Hardware
Windows 98
Printer
HP 750C
Data Source(s)
U.S. Census Bureau TIGER files and
New York City Parks Asian
longhorned beetle data
Map Type
Inventory

Traveling into the United States inside wood packing material from China, the Asian longhorned beetle (ALB) is now infesting trees in the United States. Infestation occurs when the ALB tunnels into tree stems and branches to lay eggs. Larvae develop inside the tree and then bore their way outward creating large holes in the tree's heartwood and bark.

Repeated attacks lead to the dieback of the tree crown and eventually to the death of the tree. Currently the only effective means to eliminate the ALB is to remove infested trees and destroy them by chipping.

The first U.S. infestation was discovered in Greenpoint, Brooklyn, in August 1996. A second infestation was found in Bayside, Queens, in February 1999, and later that year in August, an ALB infestation was detected in Manhattan just four blocks from Central Park.

To date, more than 2,400 infested trees have been removed from public and private property. The U.S. Department of Agriculture is presently redrawing the ALB quarantine zones based on buffers generated in ArcView GIS.

Preble's Meadow Jumping Mouse Riparian Habitat Preliminary Plan for Douglas County, Colorado

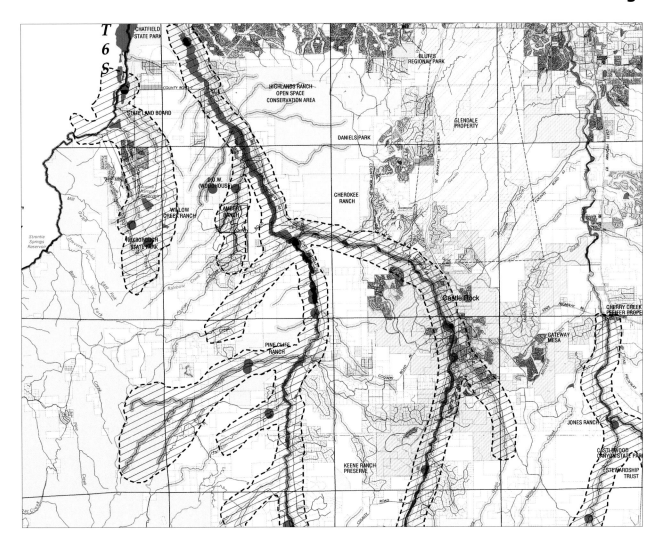

Douglas County Government
Castle Rock, Colorado

By Gail Stere

Contact
Gail Stere
gstere@douglas.co.us

Software
ArcInfo 7.2.1 and ARCPLOT

Hardware
HP

Printer
HP DesignJet 755CM

Data Source(s)
Preble's Meadow Jumping Mouse
Collaborative Project Science Team,
Colorado Division of Wildlife, Town
of Castle Rock, and ERO Resources

Map Type
Inventory

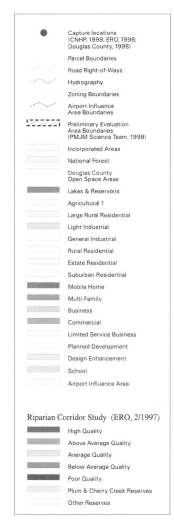

In 1998, the U.S. Fish and Wildlife Service listed the Preble's Meadow Jumping Mouse (PMJM) as a threatened species under the Endangered Species Act. Produced with GIS technology, this map displays a preliminary understanding of the mouse's habitat and its potential population distribution within Douglas County as of April 1999. This rare nocturnal mouse lives in heavily vegetated riparian areas along Colorado's Front Range. Many Douglas County stream reaches provide high-quality habitat for the mouse and could be protected as habitat under the Endangered Species Act.

Using telemetry points (red dots), the map shows locations of known mouse populations. The potential extent of mouse habitat (red shading) indicates major stream reaches throughout the county. The yellow shading illustrates potentially impacted stream corridors. The PMJM Collaborative Project Science Team defined areas known as preliminary core conservation zones and their associated buffer areas (dark cross-hatching). The underlying parcel layer identifies ownership and municipal boundaries used to determine possible issues that might limit the county's ability to develop adequate conservation measures.

The underlying parcel layer enabled the county to identify various ownership configurations and jurisdictional boundaries of affected municipalities—issues that might limit the county's ability to develop adequate conservation measures to protect the mouse.

Hurricane Surge Map for Glynn County, Georgia

Information Technology Outreach
Services, University of Georgia
Athens, Georgia

By Gary Ross

Contact
Gary Ross
gary@itos.uga.edu

Software
ArcInfo 7.2.1 and ArcView GIS

Hardware
Windows NT and UNIX

Printer
HP DesignJet 1055CM

Data Source(s)
Georgia digital line graph base map,
National Hurricane Center, and U.S.
Geological Survey

Map Type
Decision/Planning

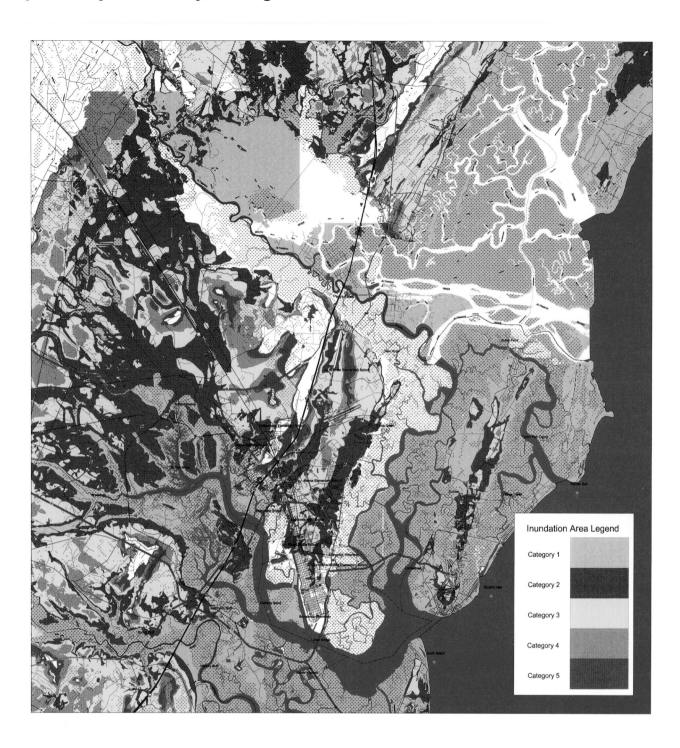

Information Technology Outreach Services (ITOS) developed and produced county-level maps for six counties along the Georgia coast. The maps show the land area susceptible to inundation by a storm surge due to hurricanes of each of the five hurricane categories.

The map data came from the National Hurricane Center's Sea, Lake, and Overland Surges from Hurricanes model. The maps also show the elevation of the land, the coastal bathymetry, and topographic elements. County emergency managers use the maps to determine the safest areas for emergency shelters and the best evacuation routes. In addition to these maps, ArcView GIS projects provide these managers with maps for on-demand analysis.

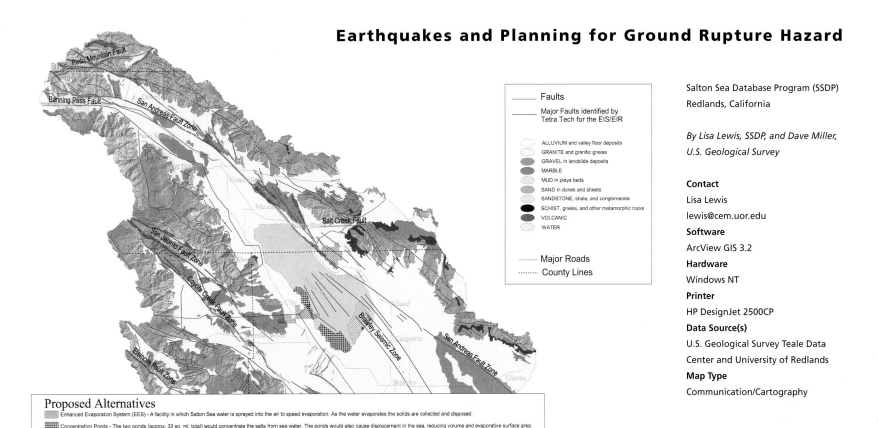

Faults

Major Faults identified by Tetra Tech for the EIS/EIR

ALLUVIUM and valley floor deposits
GRANITE and granitic gneiss
GRAVEL in landslide deposits
MARBLE
MUD in playa beds
SAND in dunes and sheets
SANDSTONE, shale, and conglomerate
SCHIST, gneiss, and other metamorphic rocks
VOLCANIC
WATER

Major Roads
County Lines

Salton Sea Database Program (SSDP)
Redlands, California

By Lisa Lewis, SSDP, and Dave Miller,
U.S. Geological Survey

Contact
Lisa Lewis
lewis@cem.uor.edu
Software
ArcView GIS 3.2
Hardware
Windows NT
Printer
HP DesignJet 2500CP
Data Source(s)
U.S. Geological Survey Teale Data
Center and University of Redlands
Map Type
Communication/Cartography

Proposed Alternatives

Enhanced Evaporation System (EES) - A facility in which Salton Sea water is sprayed into the air to speed evaporation. As the water evaporates the solids are collected and disposed.

Concentration Ponds - The two ponds (approx. 33 sq. mi. total) would concentrate the salts from sea water. The ponds would also cause displacement in the sea, reducing volume and evaporative surface area.

Displacement Dike - A dike built at the south end of the sea to reduce total volume to maintain the water elevation if inflow is reduced.

Pipelines - Pipelines that would pump out Salton Sea water to various proposed locations and pump in fresh, treated, or seawater to maintain an optimal water level and reduce salinity.

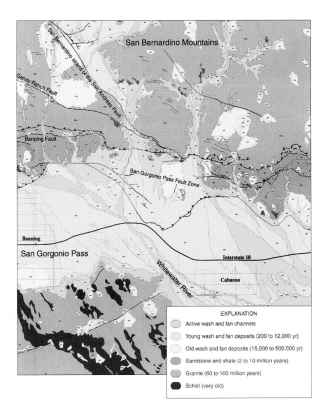

EXPLANATION

Active wash and fan channels
Young wash and fan deposits (200 to 12,000 yr)
Old wash and fan deposits (15,000 to 500,000 yr)
Sandstone and shale (2 to 10 million years)
Granite (60 to 100 million years)
Schist (very old)

Detailed maps bring a greater resolution to the number and locations of active faults. Preparing maps at a higher resolution requires extensive field study, and with a GIS, information, such as tract and parcel data, utility corridors, and flood hazard zones, can be incorporated to help decision makers in locating remediation facilities.

After the Sylmar earthquake in 1972, building codes were strengthened, and the Alquist-Priolo Special Studies Zone Act was passed. Its purpose is to mitigate the hazard of fault rupture by prohibiting the location of most human occupancy structures across the traces of active faults. Earthquake fault zones are regulatory zones that encompass surface traces of active faults with a potential for future surface fault rupture. The zones are generally established about 500 feet on either side of the surface trace of active faults.

Active faults and strips of state-mandated zoning along faults (Alquist-Priolo zones) riddle the Salton Sea Basin. The primary fault, the San Andreas, steps from the northeast side of the Salton Sea across the southern end, along a series of poorly understood faults, to the Brawley and Imperial fault systems. This stepover region has not had a historic ground-rupturing earthquake. Alquist-Priolo zones could not be defined because the faults are not well-located. Faults parallel to, and splaying from, the San Andreas are also capable of major earthquakes.

Initial plans for remediation facilities take into account the generalized information (at 1:750,000 scale) on active faults, and the fault maps do not provide information on strong ground shaking. The shaking can damage facilities that lie far from an earthquake epicenter and far from active faults. Information on near-surface materials is required to estimate the ground-shaking hazards.

Hurricane Floyd's Impact on St. Johns County, Florida

St. Johns County
St. Augustine, Florida

By Corey D. Bowens, Jeremy Bromm,
Michael J. Campbell, and Troy Nagle

Contact
Michael Campbell
gis@co.st-johns.fl.us

Software
ArcInfo 8.0.2, ArcView GIS 3.2, and
JASC Paint Shop Pro
Hardware
Windows NT and Sun Enterprise 450
server
Printer
HP DesignJet 1055CM
Data Source(s)
National Oceanic and Atmospheric
Administration, Federal Emergency
Management Agency, St. Johns
County Division of Emergency
Management, Northeast Florida
Regional Planning Council, National
Weather Service, PC Data Online,
Florida Times-Union, St. Augustine
Record, and ESRI
Map Type
Communication/Cartography

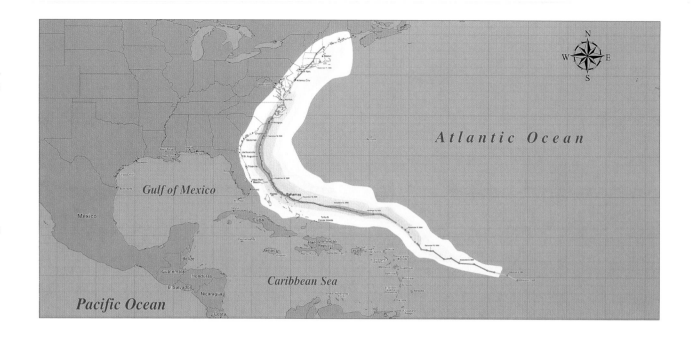

Eight major storms made 1999 a record year for hurricanes. Hurricane Floyd, a Category Four hurricane, killed 56 people in the United States and caused approximately $6 billion in damages. This map, created for the St. Johns County Division of Emergency Management, summarizes the information collected during Hurricane Floyd and shows the impact it had on St. Johns County, Florida.

During Hurricane Floyd, the St. Johns County GIS Division was responsible for the creation of maps to assist the 17 emergency support functions (ESF) of the Emergency Operations Center (EOC). The maps produced during this emergency operation depicted themes such as hurricane evacuation routes, hurricane shelter locations, hurricane evacuation zones, and mandatory evacuation areas.

Hurricane tracking data sets, including latitude, longitude, wind speed, pressure, and status, obtained from weather advisories were used to plot Hurricane Floyd's path and wind speed buffers. Storm surge data sets were plotted to assist in the real-time forecasting of hurricane storm surges based on various combinations of hurricane strength, forward speed of the storm, and direction of storm motion.

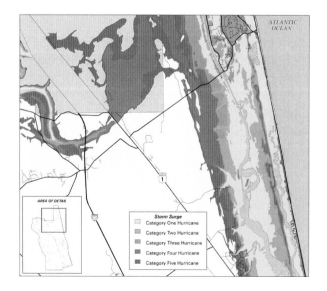

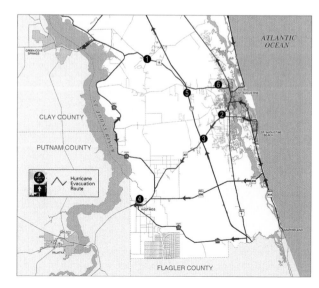

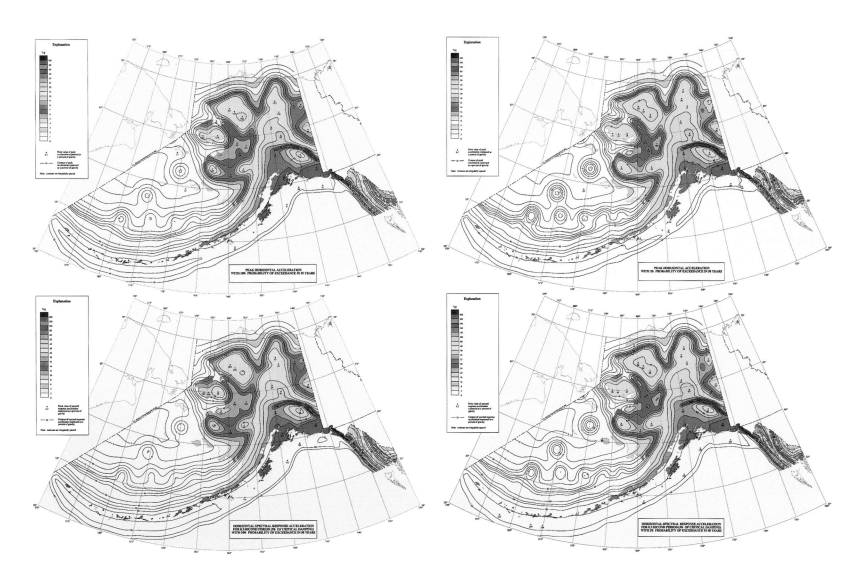

The U.S. Geological Survey produces maps of earthquake shaking hazard for the United States. The maps are based on current information about the rate at which earthquakes occur in different areas and on how far shaking extends from earthquake sources. The maps provide information essential for creating and updating the seismic design provisions of building codes used in the United States.

Scientists frequently revise these maps to reflect new knowledge. Buildings, bridges, highways, and utilities built to meet modern seismic design provisions are better able to withstand earthquakes, not only saving lives but also enabling critical activities to continue with less disruption.

U.S. Geological Survey (USGS)
Lakewood, Colorado

By Ken Rukstales and Rob Wesson

Contact
Ken Rukstales
rukstales@usgs.gov
Software
ArcInfo
Hardware
Sun Ultra 10 workstation
Printer
HP DesignJet 2500CP
Data Source(s)
USGS Seismic Hazard Mapping
Program
Map Type
Decision/Planning

Soldier Canyon Dam—Sunny Day Failure Scenario

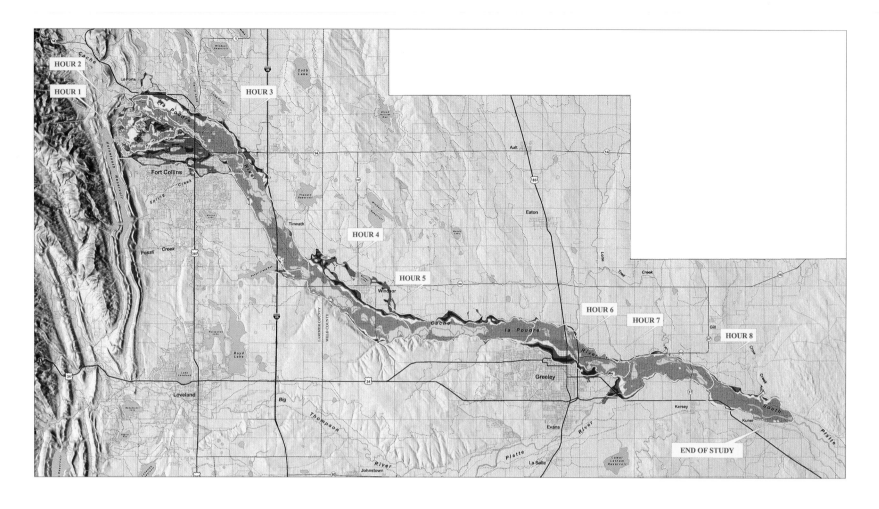

U.S. Department of the Interior,
Bureau of Reclamation
Mid-Pacific Region,
MPGIS Service Center
Sacramento, California;
Denver Technical Service Center
Denver, Colorado

By Bruce Feinberg, Tom Heinzer, and
Kurt Wille

Contact
Kurt Wille
kwille@do.usbr.gov
Software
ArcInfo, ArcView GIS,
and MIKE 21 (DHI)
Hardware
HP-UX and Windows NT
Printer
HP DesignJet 2500CP
Data Source(s)
Internal
Map Type
Modeling/Analytical

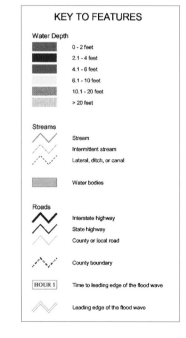

KEY TO FEATURES

Water Depth
- 0 - 2 feet
- 2.1 - 4 feet
- 4.1 - 6 feet
- 6.1 - 10 feet
- 10.1 - 20 feet
- > 20 feet

Streams
- Stream
- Intermittent stream
- Lateral, ditch, or canal

- Water bodies

Roads
- Interstate highway
- State highway
- County or local road

- County boundary

HOUR 1 Time to leading edge of the flood wave

Leading edge of the flood wave

This map was produced in ArcView GIS as part of a study of Soldier Canyon Dam in Fort Collins, Colorado. The study was performed using ArcInfo with MIKE 21 as the main hydrodynamic model. The U.S. Bureau of Reclamation Technical Services Center in Denver, Colorado, conducted the study.

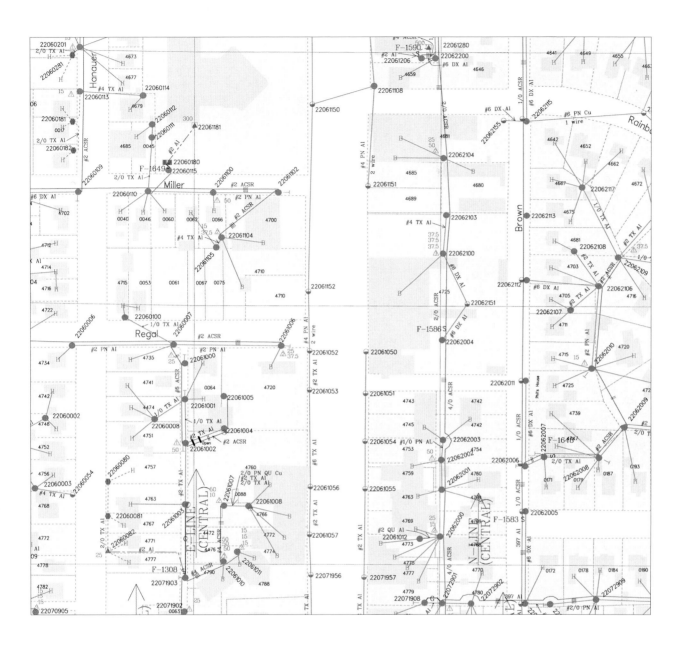

Murray City Power
Murray, Utah

By Janie Richardson

Contact
Janie Richardson
jrichardson@ci.murray.ut.us
Software
ArcInfo 8.0.2
Hardware
Dell Pentium III PC
Printer
HP DesignJet 2500CP
Data Source(s)
ArcInfo Power Line arc, node, and
point feature coverages
Map Type
Inventory

The Wiring and Device map is a facilities location map used by Murray City Power field crews to identify and locate power infrastructure features. ARC Macro Language programs and systems are used to generate each map for the department.

Each map covers a quarter section of the city and shows power features, parcel lines, building footprints, and street names. Power features identified on the map use symbology, unique feature ID labels, and coverage annotation.

GIS Map Classified by Type of Residential Customers in Pomprabsatrupai

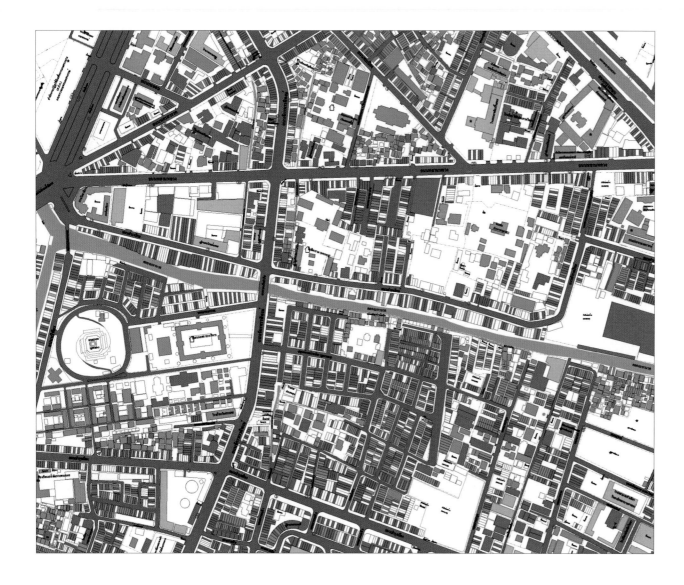

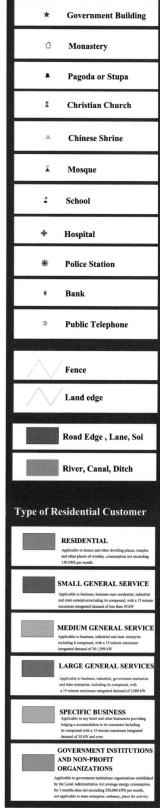

★	Government Building
⌂	Monastery
▲	Pagoda or Stupa
⚊	Christian Church
⌃	Chinese Shrine
⚇	Mosque
♪	School
✚	Hospital
✳	Police Station
$	Bank
☏	Public Telephone

/\/\	Fence
/\/\	Land edge

■	Road Edge , Lane, Soi
■	River, Canal, Ditch

Type of Residential Customer

RESIDENTIAL
Applicable to homes and other dwelling places, temples and other places of worship ,consumption not exceeding 150 kWh per month.

SMALL GENERAL SERVICE
Applicable to business, business cum residential, industrial and state enterpriseincluding its compound, with a 15 minute maximum integrated demand of less than 30 kW

MEDIUM GENERAL SERVICE
Applicable to business, industrial and state enterprise including it compound, with a 15-minute maximum integrated demand of 30-1,999 kW

LARGE GENERAL SERVICES
Applicable to business, industrial, government institution and state enterprise, including its compound, with a 15-minute maximum integrated demand of 2,000 kW

SPECIFIC BUSINESS
Applicable to any hotel and other businesses providing lodging a accomodation to its customers including its compound with a 15-minute maximum integrated demand of 30 kW and over.

GOVERNMENT INSTITUTIONS AND NON-PROFIT ORGANIZATIONS
Applicable to government institutions organizations established by the Local Administration Act average energy consumption for 3 months does not exceeding 250,000 kWh per month, not applicable to state enterprise, embassy, place for activity.

Metropolitan Electricity Authority (MEA)
Bangkok, Thailand

By Kanjana Anuvanitruttavate and Araya Senchawanich

Contact
Araya Senchawanich
gis@mea.or.th
Software
ArcInfo 7.2.1 and ArcView GIS 3.1
Hardware
Sun workstation and Windows 98
Printer
HP DesignJet 750C
Data Source(s)
MEA GIS database
Map Type
Decision/Planning

This map was designed for a Customer Electrical Load Profile Analysis proposed in Pomprabsatrupai, a part of Bangkok with a major electrical distribution network supplied by underground cable. Customers are classified in six types—residential, small general service, medium general service, large general service, specific business and government institutions, and nonprofit organizations.

The map will be used for load forecasting analysis and long-term planning as well as studying other related effects from investment and construction of electrical equipment such as substations, poles, and conductors. The map also shows the direction of growth and a demographic profile of the city.

Estimating Pollutant Load Reduction Targets

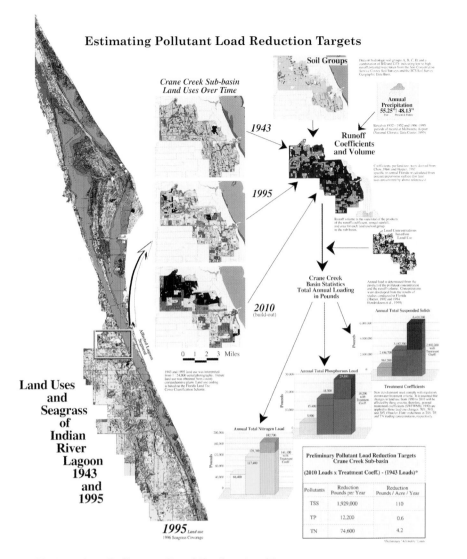

Spatial Analysis of Changes in Basin, Land Use, and Seagrass

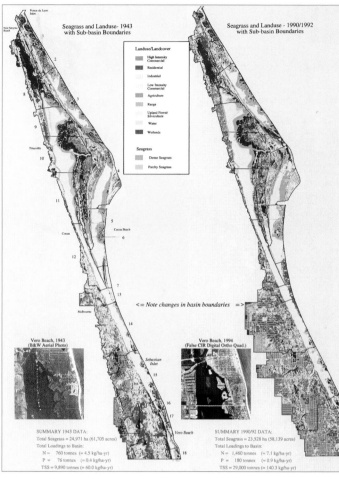

Estimating Pollutant Load Reduction Targets

Seagrass-based pollutant load reduction targets are a major objective of the Indian River Lagoon (IRL) restoration program. In the Crane Creek Basin, major source data sets for this model are land use coverages generated from aerial photography and a 2010 or build out land use derived from comprehensive growth plans provided by local governments. Soil type and annual precipitation are also incorporated into the model to produce runoff volume.

Pounds of pollutants per year are calculated by multiplying the volume of runoff by literature-based pollutant concentrations. These annual loadings for total phosphorus (TP), total nitrogen (TN), and total suspended solids (TSS) are shown in multicolored bar graphs and quantified in the table.

Spatial Analysis of Changes in Basin, Land Use, and Seagrass

This display illustrates the connection between land development and seagrass response in a portion of the Indian River Lagoon. Two maps of the St. Johns River Water Management District's portion of the lagoon basin show land use in 1943 with seagrass beds and land use in 1992 with seagrass beds. Agricultural drainage and canals are responsible for the large increase in area of the southern basin. ESRI's software generated all of the maps and enabled seamless calculations of the change analysis.

Jones Edmunds and Associates and St. Johns River Water Management District
Gainesville, Florida

By Ed Carter, W. Green, and
J.S. Steward (Estimating)
Ed Carter, D. Samuel Rajasekhar, and
Robert W. Virnstein (Spatial Analysis)

Contact
Ed Carter
ecarter@jea.net
Software
ArcInfo and ArcView GIS
Hardware
UNIX
Printer
HP DesignJet 750C
Data Source(s)
St. Johns River Water Management
District acoustic soundings
Map Type
Modeling/Analytical

Mapping Historic Hoh Channelization Patterns

Channel Migration on the Lower Hoh River

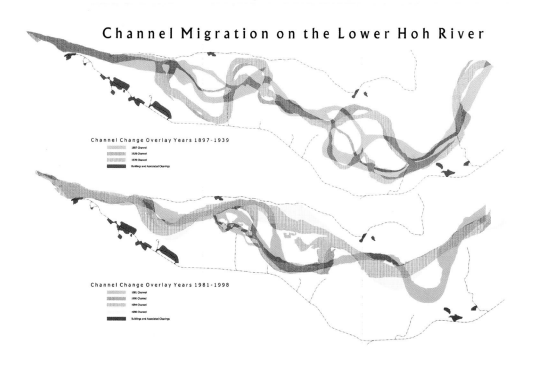

Channel Change Overlay Years 1897-1939

Channel Change Overlay Years 1981-1998

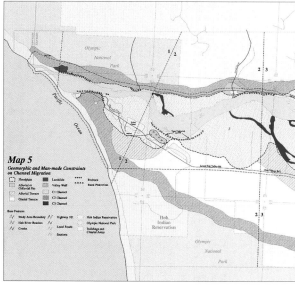

Map 5
Geomorphic and Man-made Constraints on Channel Migration

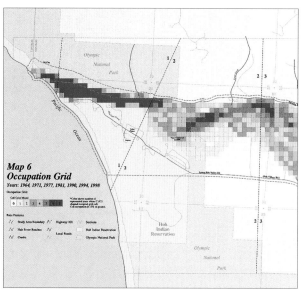

Map 6
Occupation Grid
Years: 1964, 1971, 1977, 1981, 1990, 1994, 1998

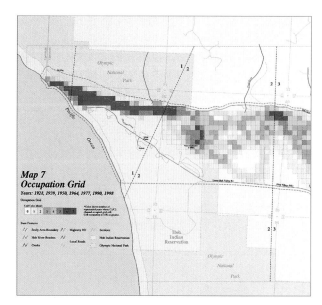

Map 7
Occupation Grid
Years: 1928, 1939, 1950, 1964, 1977, 1990, 1998

TerraLogic GIS
Stanwood, Washington

By Jane Cassady and Chris Hansen

Contact
Jane Cassady
janec@terralogicgis.com
Software
ArcInfo and ArcView GIS
Hardware
Windows NT and UNIX
Printer
HP DesignJet 650C
Data Source(s)
Developed in-house
Map Type
Modeling/Analytical

TerraLogic, in collaboration with Perkins GeoScience, developed GIS methods and protocols for assessing channel movement in the lower reaches of the Hoh River using time series aerial photography and hardcopy maps (1897–1998).

To help evaluate historic channel movement and the role woody debris plays in the lower reaches of the Hoh, TerraLogic built digital coverages detailing historic channel and woody debris locations and produced a series of technical maps to help field truthing efforts.

TerraLogic is currently conducting channel migration analyses and producing final report graphics. The analyses include change in active channel area, change in channel structure, channel constraint locations, channel movement, and an occupation grid.

The U.S. Department of Interior, Bureau of Indian Affairs and the Hoh Indian Tribe funded this project.

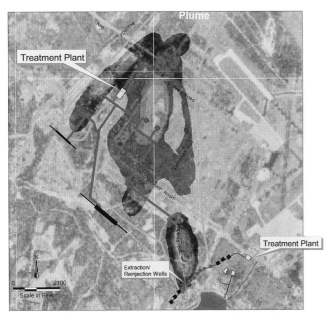

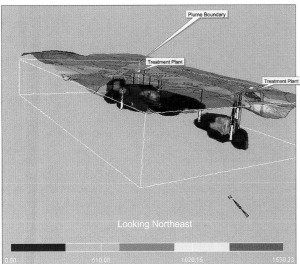

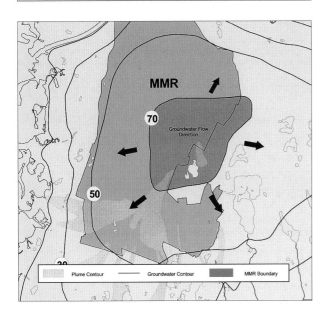

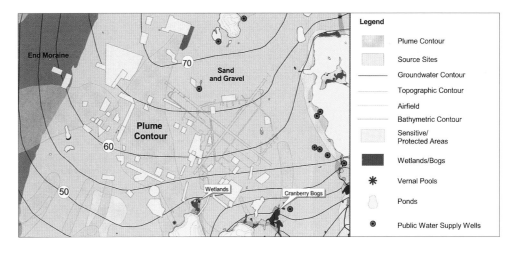

The Massachusetts Military Reservation (MMR) is located on Cape Cod, Massachusetts, and is one of the largest U.S. Department of Defense Superfund sites in the United States. Military activities have contributed to hundreds of contaminant sources and more than a dozen contaminant plumes in the area, and because the military base is located at the top of the region's sole source aquifer and near sensitive and protected habitats, it is of immediate concern.

In 1996, Jacobs Engineering began remediation of the subsurface contamination at MMR. This involved the development of a large chemical database that has been incorporated into a GIS containing environmental, municipal, and engineering data from multiple sources.

The GIS enables users to access data from each of these sources and analyze changes in compound concentrations and spatial distributions over time with respect to surrounding environmental data. Three-dimensional plume shells that have been modeled using Groundwater Modeling System, along with particle track information and base map data, provide a comprehensive assessment of site changes and remediation progress.

This output can be easily communicated to the public by showing the current and predicted relationship of the plumes to the remediation systems and surrounding environment. The ability to use GIS in combination with these programs enables interactive assessments of the groundwater plumes and their surrounding environments.

Jacobs Engineering
Otis Air National Guard Base,
Massachusetts

By Jessica Baker

Contact
Jessica Baker
jbaker42@hotmail.com
Software
ArcInfo, ArcView GIS, ArcView
3D Analyst, ArcView Spatial Analyst,
Groundwater Modeling System, and
Advanced Visual Systems
Hardware
Windows NT
Printer
HP DesignJet 2500CP
Data Source(s)
Massachusetts GIS data layers,
Jacobs Engineering chemical data,
and three-dimensional modeled
plume data
Map Type
Modeling/Analytical

Land Use Runoff Contributions to Marine Water Bodies, Sinclair Inlet and Dyes Inlet, Kitsap County, Washington

Concurrent Technologies Corporation
Bremerton, Washington

By Dirk Vandervoort

Contact
Dirk Vandervoort
vandervoort@ctc.com

Software
ArcView GIS

Hardware
Windows NT

Printer
HP DesignJet 755CM

Data Source(s)
University of Washington Libraries,
Oregon Climate Service, and
proprietary interpretation of Landsat
Thematic Mapper imagery

Map Type
Modeling/Analytical

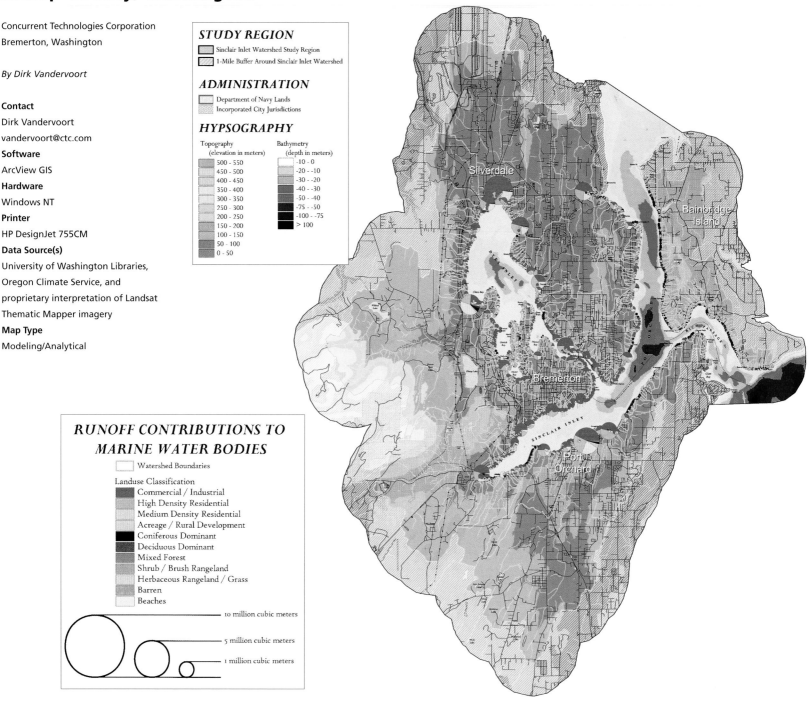

This map represents the results of GIS contributions to a watershed-based study that is assessing risk to ecological resources in Sinclair Inlet and surrounding marine water bodies. The map is a portrayal of modeled surface water runoff entering marine water bodies at pour points from upland drainage systems. Pie charts show the relative contributions of land use classes that potentially affect water quality at each of the pour points. The size of the pie chart is proportional to the modeled water discharge at each pour point.

The analysis presented in this map indicates that while runoff from a few large-order/well-integrated drainage systems contribute water from a variety of land use classes (both urban and rural), numerous low-order/less-integrated drainage systems adjacent to marine water bodies contribute significant volumes of water from mostly urban land use classes.

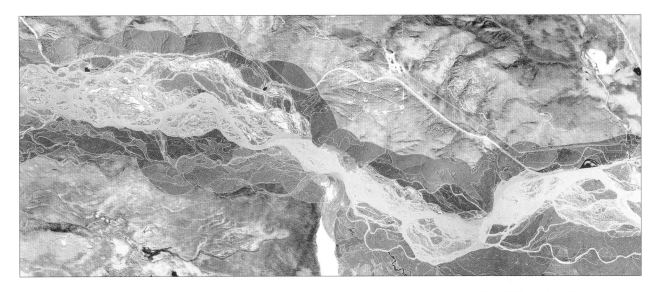

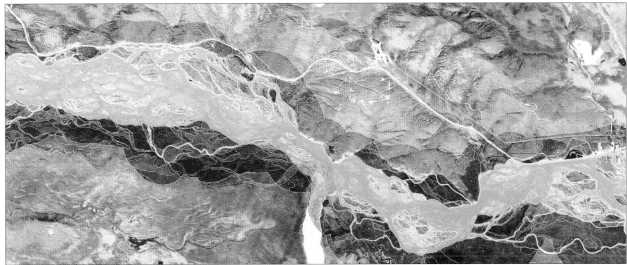

Tanana Chiefs Conference, Inc.
Alaska Department of Natural
Resources, Division of Forestry
Fairbanks, Alaska

*By Dave Burns, Robert Ott,
Will Putman, and Gordon Worum*

Contact
Will Putman
wputman@tananachiefs.org

Software
ArcInfo 7.2.1 and PCI OrthoEngine
Hardware
Sun Solaris and Windows NT
Printer
HP DesignJet 2500CP
Data Source(s)
Landsat Thematic Mapper imagery,
Indian resource satellite imagery,
colored infrared aerial photography,
and State of Alaska vegetation type
polygon vectors
Map Type
Decision/Planning

The Alaska Department of Natural Resources, Division of Forestry and Tanana Chiefs Conference, Inc., Forestry Program are cooperating on a study of Tanana River bank erosion patterns. The state of Alaska Department of Environmental Conservation provides funding support. Forestry and fishery management issues in the Tanana River basin have generated interest in erosion patterns of the Tanana River from regulatory and management agencies as well as the public. This interest comes with the realization that there is scant quantitative data about issues such as acreage loss to erosion in various cover types, large woody debris recruitment rates, and relative bank stability along different sections of the river.

This study analyzes the banks of the Tanana River using GIS installations at both cooperating organizations. The study area includes the land along the entire Tanana River within one-half mile of the riverbanks between the communities of Tanana and Northway, a reach of about 480 miles.

Riverbank changes will be examined in the context of geomorphic and surficial geologic features to determine if different land management strategies may be more or less appropriate in different riparian areas in the Tanana River drainage.

Known Fish Habitat Areas for Listed Species in Multnomah County, Oregon

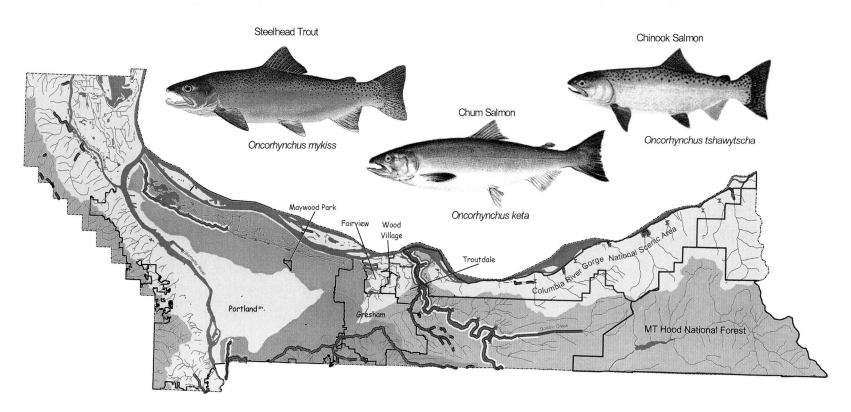

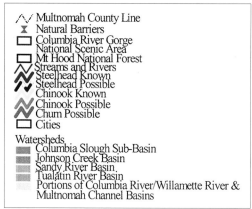

Multnomah County GIS
Resource Center
Portland, Oregon

By Jeffrey Gilmour

Contact
Karen Harris
karen.l.harris@co.multnomah.or.us
Software
ArcView GIS 3.2
Hardware
Windows NT
Printer
HP DesignJet 750C+ and
HP DesignJet 8500N
Data Source(s)
Multnomah County GIS Resource
Center and Metro Data Resource
Center
Map Type
Decision/Planning, Inventory

The Endangered Species Act (ESA) listed several species of salmon native to the Columbia River basin in northwestern United States. They are Lower Columbia River chinook salmon, Columbia River chum salmon, and Lower Columbia River steelhead trout.

The northern border of Multnomah County, Oregon, is the Columbia River. During an 18-month period, the county and consultants prepared a document describing Multnomah County's ESA/Salmon Recovery Planning efforts. These images are some of the maps included in that document.

The first step of the planning effort was to inventory county program areas and activities that could potentially affect steelhead trout and salmon. Maps were prepared to show city and government jurisdictions within the habitat areas, watershed boundaries, the distribution of each endangered species within the watersheds, natural barriers such as waterfalls, and fish runs and habitat reaches.

The map series is used extensively in analysis and decision making for county operation and watershed restoration programs. The map layers are integrated with other GIS inventories, such as fish passage culverts, and provide spatial analysis on issues relating to fish recovery.

County staff, other agencies, and the public use these maps, which provide quick and complete habitat definitions that are generally complex and difficult to visualize.

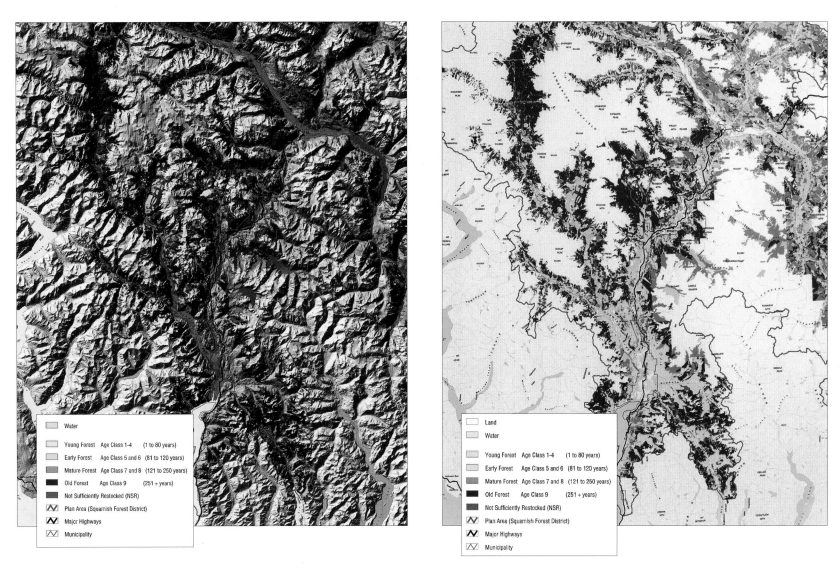

The Sea-to-Sky Land and Resource Management Plan is a regional land use planning process for Crown lands within the Squamish Forest District north of Vancouver, British Columbia, Canada. Its goal is to produce an integrated land and resource management plan that addresses a range of land and resource uses and interests.

This map, which shows forest cover classified into age classes, is one of a series of resource theme maps produced as part of the land use and resource inventory to support the planning process. The map depicts the potential forest resources in the plan area and also terrain-related constraints that could limit harvesting opportunities. The Squamish Forest District has rugged terrain with elevations ranging from sea level to 2,500 meters that makes many areas within the district unsuitable for logging.

A shaded relief method illustrates the forest age classes, which enables users to visualize the topography of the area. The shaded relief was created with a 25-meter digital elevation model and is the backdrop for the forest age classes.

British Columbia Ministry of Environment Lands and Parks Surrey, British Columbia, Canada

By Gurdeep Singh

Contact
Gurdeep Singh
gurdeep.singh@gems2.gov.bc.ca
Software
ArcInfo 8.0.2
Hardware
UNIX
Printer
HP DesignJet 1055CM
Data Source(s)
Corporate and regional data warehouses
Map Type
Inventory

Modeling Population, Agriculture, and Infrastructure Under Natural Hazard

Earth Satellite Corporation
Rockville, Maryland

By Jeffrey B. Miller

Contact
Jeffrey Miller
jmiller@earthsat.com

Software
ArcInfo 8, ArcView GIS 3.2, ERDAS
IMAGINE 8.1, and SCO X-Vision

Hardware
Dual Intel Xeon 500, Sun Enterprise
4000 server

Printer
HP DesignJet 3500CP

Data Source(s)
National Oceanic and Atmospheric
Administration, U.S. Geological
Survey, Digital Chart of the World,
International Geosphere Biosphere
Program, U.S. Census Bureau, and
Earth Satellite Corporation

Map Type
Modeling/Analytical

South Asia Population Density 1998

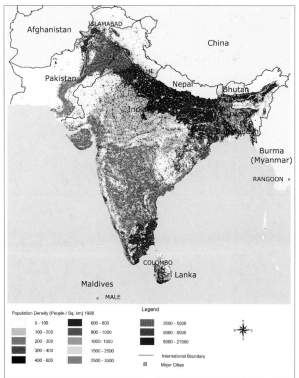

South Asia Primeness of Agricultural Lands

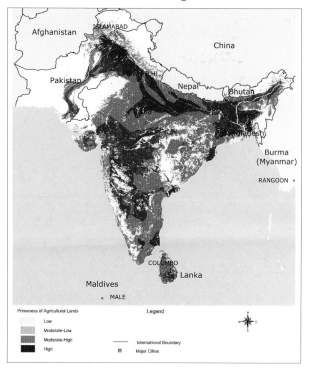

South Asia Cyclonic Storm Hazard Zones

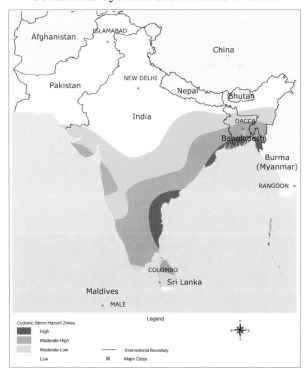

Earth Satellite Corporation (EarthSat) worked with iSciences, LLC, of Ann Arbor, Michigan, to develop a GIS that synthesizes the relationship of regional population increase, the value of sustaining agriculture, and the natural hazards (earthquakes, tsunamis, volcanoes, and cyclonic storms), which threaten them.

South Asia Population Density 1998 shows the distribution of population per square kilometer throughout south Asia. EarthSat developed an ArcInfo multicriteria population distribution model that allocates U.S. Census Bureau International Division population estimates to a one-kilometer resolution surface. National Oceanic and Atmospheric Administration (NOAA) Defense Meteorological Satellite Program persistent nighttime lights, regional urban and transportation density, proximity to Digital Chart of the World (DCW) settlement locations, and International Geosphere Biosphere (IGBP) land use/land cover serve as allocation criteria.

South Asia Primeness of Agricultural Lands shows the landscape's potential suitability for agricultural use. EarthSat's ArcInfo multicriteria GIS models soil type, access to soil moisture, slope, and access to food demand centers to map composite agricultural primeness. IGBP land cover, DCW transportation and drainage networks, U.S. Geological Survey GTOPO30 elevation, and NOAA precipitation serve as model inputs to characterize these components.

South Asia Cyclonic Storm Hazard Zones portrays the historic density and magnitude of typhoons and tropical depressions throughout south Asia. EarthSat uses historic NOAA storm tracks to model the regional density of cyclonic storms weighted by reported storm intensity.

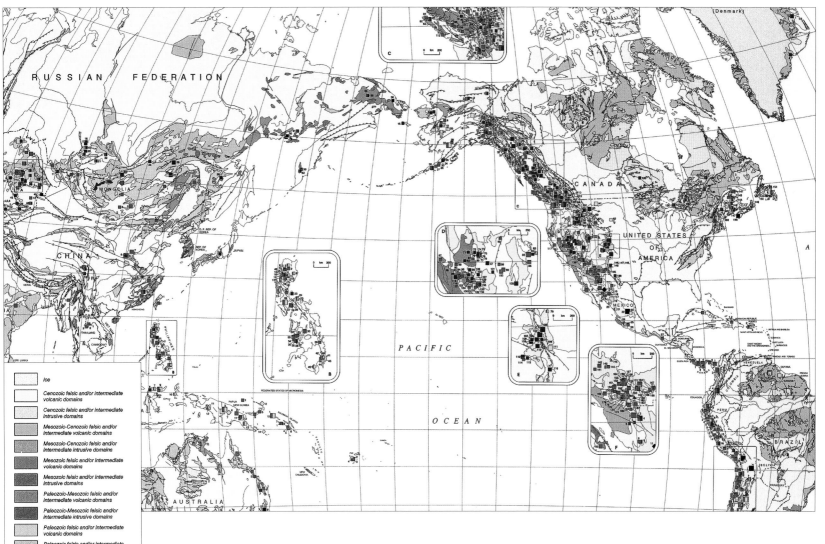

This map, which depicts porphyry-related deposits, its underlying database, and the generalized geology of the world as a backdrop, is part of the World Map project. The symbolization of deposit subtypes on the map was generated from the underlying database, which was compiled in Microsoft Access. The file was converted, and an ArcInfo coverage of the deposits was generated using geographic coordinates. ARC Macro Language (AML) plotted the deposits, the insets, and the deposit listings in the surroundings using the INFO data file as the information source.

An AML script was also used for plotting the generalized geology coverage as a backdrop. AML routines prepared this coverage, which apply a set of age and specialized rock type queries to the full Generalized Geology of the World GIS database, attach corresponding generalized classifiers to a copy of the bedrock domain coverage, and dissolve all redundant arcs. For other thematic views of the geology, click on the "Images of World Geology" at www.nrcan.gc.ca/gsc/mrd/wmgdb.

Natural Resources Canada
Ottawa, Ontario, Canada

By L.B. Chorlton, K.P.E. Dunne, R.V. Kirkham, and M.G. Méthot

Contact
Mario Méthot
mmethot@nrcan.gc.ca
Software
ArcInfo 7.2.1
Hardware
Sun Solaris workstation
Printer
HP2000
Data Source(s)
Author and Generalized Geology of the World GIS database
Map Type
Communication/Cartography

Magnetic Field of the Earth

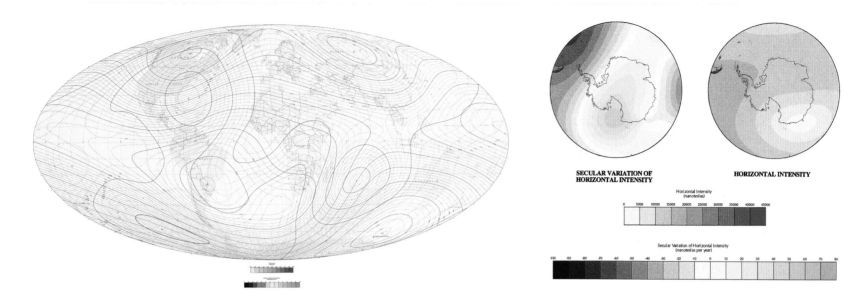

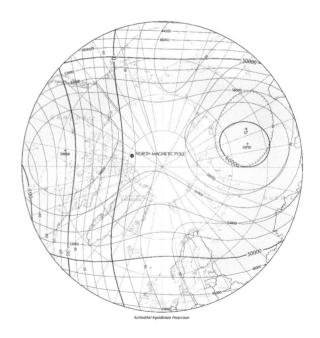

U.S. Geological Survey (USGS)
Lakewood, Colorado

By John Quinn and Ken Rukstales

Contact
Ken Rukstales
rukstales@usgs.gov
Software
ArcInfo 8
Hardware
Windows Intel
Printer
HP DesignJet 2500CP
Data Source(s)
ArcWorld™ and USGS National
Geomagnetic Information Center
Map Type
Modeling/Analytical

The Earth's magnetic field, as measured by a magnetic sensor above the Earth's surface, is a composite of several magnetic fields generated by a variety of sources. These fields are superimposed on each other and through inductive processes interact with each other. The most important of these sources are (1) the Earth's conductive, fluid core; (2) the Earth's crust and upper mantle; (3) the ionosphere; and (4) the magnetosphere.

The Earth's outer core generates more than 95 percent of the geomagnetic field. This portion of the geomagnetic field is represented by the 2000 International Geomagnetic Reference Field (IGRF) charts. The IGRF model and its secular variation (annual change) consist of a spherical harmonic equation of degree and order 10. This equation is based on several proposed geomagnetic models, which are weighted according to their judged validity. The IGRF model and its secular variation are updated every five years. Each model is valid from its base year through the next five years.

The IGRF and other geomagnetic models are used for several navigational and global positioning applications including air and sea navigation, satellite positioning, and GPS readers and recorders. It is also used for geophysical investigations of the Earth's crust, mantle, core, ionosphere, magnetosphere, and magnetic anomalies.

The IGRF charts are a series of five maps that depict the inclination, declination, horizontal intensity, vertical intensity, and total intensity of the Earth's magnetic field.

HORIZONTAL INTENSITY

**SECULAR VARIATION OF
HORIZONTAL INTENSITY**

Geology of Tasmania

Minerals Resources Tasmania
Hobart, Tasmania, Australia

*By A.V. Brown, C.R. Calver,
M.J. Clarke, K.D. Corbett,
J.L. Everard, S.M. Forsyth,
B.A. Goscombe, G.R. Green,
M.P. McClenaghan, J. Pemberton,
and D.B. Seymour*

Contact
Ken Bird
kbird@mrt.tas.gov.au
Software
ArcInfo 7.2.1
Hardware
Sun Ultra 2 workstation
Printer
HP DesignJet 2500CP
Data Source(s)
Tasmanian Geological Survey
Geological Atlas 1:250,000 digital
series of maps and other sources
Map Type
Communication/Cartography

Mineral Resources Tasmania produces a range of products to assist the mining exploration industry and the public. These products include geological maps, in both hard-copy and digital formats, and an extensive range of geological reports.

The Geology of Tasmania map gives a concise overview of Tasmanian geology and is used widely by the public, the government, and the mining industry.

Digital Shasta—Applying GIS Technology to Volcano Hazards

U.S. Geological Survey (USGS)
Menlo Park, California

By Richard Blakely,
Robert Christiansen, David Ramsey,
Joel Robinson, and James Smith

Contact
David Ramsey
dramsey@usgs.gov
Software
ArcInfo 7.2.1, ARC GRID, and
ArcView GIS 3.2
Hardware
Sun Ultra Enterprise 4000 UNIX
workstation and Windows NT
Printer
HP DesignJet 2500CP
Data Source(s)
USGS, U.S. Census Bureau, and ESRI
Map Type
Decision/Planning

The U.S. Geological Survey (USGS) Volcano Hazards at Mount Shasta project is charged with mapping the geology and assessing the volcano hazards of the Mount Shasta region. Mount Shasta was chosen for study because it is the largest Cascade Range stratocone volcano and has produced more documented eruptions in the past 4,000 years than any Cascades' volcano other than Mount St. Helens.

At 14,161 feet, Mount Shasta is the highest and most recognizable landmark in northern California. Its snow and glacier covered summit dominates the skyline. It is also potentially the most dangerous volcano in northern California and one of the most dangerous in the Cascade Range, a chain of volcanoes that stretches from British Columbia to California. Future eruption activity from Mount Shasta could threaten people's lives and property and could hinder or cut off travel through the Shasta region, the major transportation corridor between California and the Pacific Northwest.

The geologic map consists of 1:24,000-scale mapping of the geology of nine USGS 7.5-minute quadrangles. The project is still in progress, and when completed the mapping will cover parts of 35 USGS 7.5-minute quadrangles. The geology was mapped in the field on USGS 7.5-minute quadrangles and compiled as a digital map database in ArcInfo. These field sheets were cut into four pieces each to help eliminate distortion. The pieces were individually scanned, transformed into ArcInfo grids, and georegistered. The grids served as the raster background over which the vector geologic coverages were digitized in ArcInfo.

This work resulted in a detailed database that can easily be compared to and combined with other geospatial data, such as U.S. Census Bureau population figures, slope calculations, and elevation data, to visualize and analyze volcano hazards and their potential effects at Mount Shasta.

Basement Surface

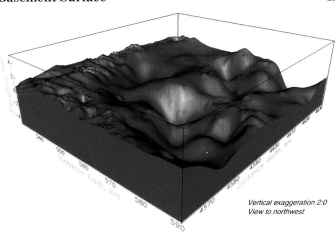

Inside Mount Shasta

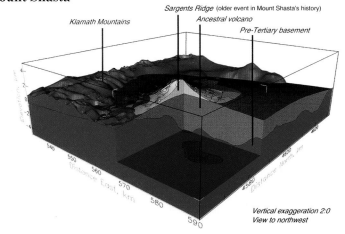

Klamath Mountains

Sargents Ridge (older event in Mount Shasta's history)
Ancestral volcano
Pre-Tertiary basement

Vertical exaggeration 2:0
View to northwest

Population

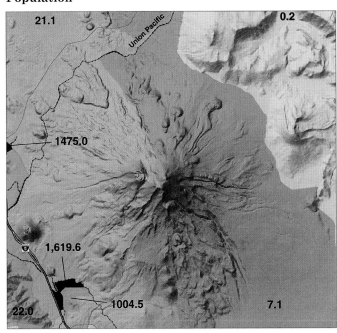

21.1

0.2

Union Pacific

1475.0

1,619.6

22.0

1004.5

7.1

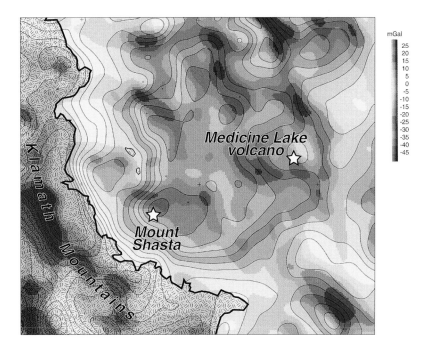

mGal

25
20
15
10
5
0
-5
-10
-15
-20
-25
-30
-35
-40
-45

Klamath Mountains

Medicine Lake volcano

Mount Shasta

Lava Flows

Pyroclastic Flows

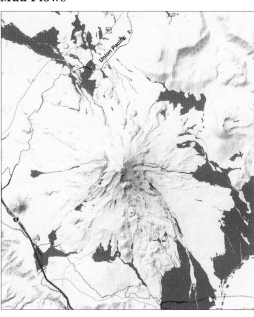

Mud Flows

Mapping Mars

The Isidis Plains Unit, Mars: Possible Catastrophic Origin, Tectonic Tilting, and Sediment Loading

Three-Dimensional Shaded Relief Map of Isidis Plains Unit

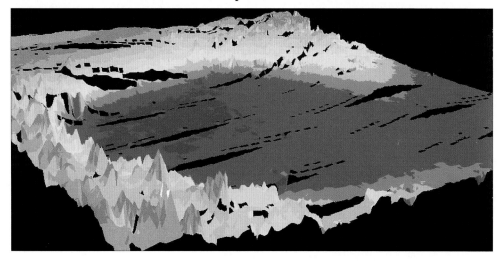

Topographic Contours, Isidis Plains Unit Contact, and Contact Elevations

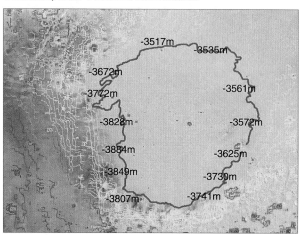

U.S. Geological Survey
Flagstaff, Arizona

By Eric Kolb and Kenneth Tanaka
(MOLA), Taylor Joyal, Kenneth
Tanaka, and Alisa Wenker (Isidis)

Contact
Trent Hare
thare@usgs.gov
Software
ArcView GIS and ISIS image
processing software (MOLA),
ArcView Spatial Analyst, ArcView
3D Analyst, and PEDR2TAB (Isidis)
Hardware
Windows and UNIX
Printer
HP DesignJet 755CM
Data Source(s)
Viking I, Viking II, Mars Global
Surveyor, Mars Laser Altimeter
(MOLA), and Mars Orbiter Camera
(MOC)
Map Type
Communication/Cartography

The Isidis Plains Unit, Mars: Possible Catastrophic Origin, Tectonic Tilting, and Sediment Loading

The map authors proposed that the plains material within Isidis Planitia formed as the result of catastrophic erosion of Syrtis Major Planum along the western edge of the basin. Such a singular event could have led to the formation of mud volcanoes in the basin because of the expansive release of trapped volatiles from beneath and within the deposits. The Mars Orbital Laser Altimeter (MOLA) data showed that the basin is not flat but lower in the southwestern part.

If the plains deposit was initially flat or sloping up toward Syrtis Major Planum, the present topography could result from lithospheric sagging because of basin infilling and/or from tilting due to loading of a huge "mud ocean" deposit within Utopia Planitia.

What Can MOLA Reveal About the South Polar Layered Deposits?

Elevation data acquired by MOLA, geologic mapping observations, and estimates for load-induced lithospheric sagging were synthesized to improve thickness and volume estimates for the south polar layer deposits (SPLD) on Mars. The results indicate a minimum SPLD volume of 1.6 by 106 km^3 and a maximum volume of 2.3 to 2.4 by 106 km^3.

What Can MOLA Reveal About the South Polar Layered Deposits?

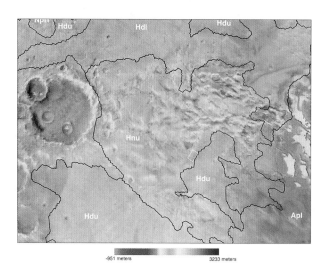

Civil Engineering Department, Drainage GIS Section, Ministry of Municipal Affairs and Agriculture Doha, Qatar

By GIS Division, Drainage Department, Ministry of Municipal Affairs and Agriculture

Contact
Yasser Al Noor
yassern@gisqatar.org.qa
Software
ArcInfo 7.0.4
Hardware
Digital UNIX
Printer
HP DesignJet 750C
Data Source(s)
Drainage Department coverages
Map Type
Communication/Cartography

شبكة الصرف الصحي
DRAINAGE NETWORK

LEGEND		الدليل
Foul Sewer Network		شبكة مجاري
Foul Sewer		خط مجاري
Rising Main		خطوط ضخ الصرف الصحي
House Connection		خطوط توصيلات المنازل
Manhole		غرفة تفتيش
Manhole One		غرفة تفتيش ١
Discharge Chamber		غرفة تفريغ أوسام
Pump Station		محطة ضخ
Surface/Ground Water Network		شبكة المياه السطحية والجوفية
Sewer		خط صرف صحي
Gully Connection		خطوط توصيلات المنازل
Manhole		غرفة تفتيش
Gully		مصرف مياه الأمطار
Treated Effluent Network		شبكة مياه الصرف الصحي المعالجة
Treated Effluent		خطوط مياه المعالجة
Main Chamber		حجرة رئيسية
Distribution Chamber		حجرة توزيع
Pump Station		محطة ضخ
Water Tower		برج مياه

This map depicts the area of Khalifa Town (South) in Qatar and illustrates the Qatar National Drainage Network. Qatar's Drainage Department is responsible for creating and maintaining a detailed wastewater collection, conveyance, treatment, and reuse database.

Coordinates for these drainage features are accurate to within 20 centimeters. Showing sewage, surface/groundwater, and treated effluent networks, this map is typically referred to by the engineers and surveyors of the Drainage Department to carry out their day-to-day activities including maintenance on existing drainage features, construction work of new drainage infrastructure, closed-circuit television survey work, and inspection of sewage flow.

Spatial attribute information for individual drainage features is also available in a separate database. This map's base layer of urban data was created and is maintained by the Center for Geographic Information Systems in Qatar through which all government agencies share their data.

Thematic Maps Representing Housing and Population Distribution

Statistical Department, The Planning
Council, The State of Qatar
Doha, Qatar

By Mansoor Al Malki and
Dr. R.C.S. Taragi

Contact
R.C.S. Taragi
taragi@planning.gov.qa

Software
ArcInfo 7
Hardware
UNIX workstation
Printer
HP DesignJet 650C
Data Source(s)
1997 Qatar Housing and Population
Census and Qatar GIS database
Map Type
Communication/Cartography

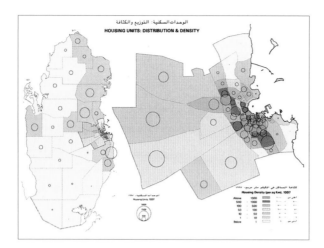

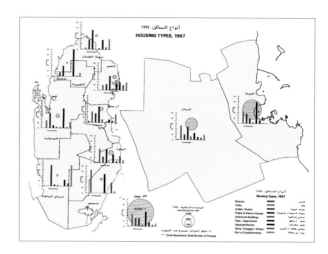

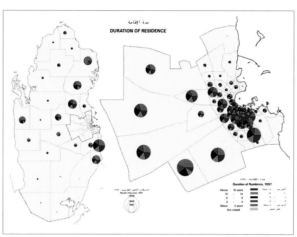

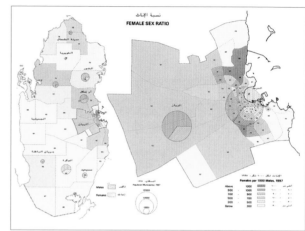

Thematic representation of different kinds of attributes and statistical information through maps and diagrams is valuable to a variety of data users. A thematic map enables the statistics to speak through visual representation of the facts and further enables their geographic interpretation.

The main objective of these maps is to demonstrate the capability of GIS in statistical analysis and representation of themes in terms of their geographic distribution and interrelationships. These thematic maps representing some of the housing and population characteristics in Qatar are based on the general population and housing census conducted by the country in 1997.

All the maps are prepared through ARC Macro Language programming in ArcInfo. The attribute (statistical) data is tied to its spatial unit and displayed using different techniques of thematic mapping. The methodology for representation varies from one map to another and includes the dot method of population distribution to choropleth mapping and representation through different types of charts.

Kids' Care Connections Child Care and Transportation Map

Delaware Valley Child Care Council
(DVCCC)
Philadelphia, Pennsylvania

*By Kathy O'Connor, DVCCC, and
Kevin Switala, Gannett Fleming*

Contact
Kevin Switala
kswitala@gfnet.com
Software
ArcView GIS 3.1 and 3.2
Hardware
Windows NT
Printer
HP DesignJet 755CM
Data Source(s)
Southeastern Pennsylvania Transit
Authority; Etak, Inc.; and DVCCC
Map Type
Communication/Cartography

The Delaware Valley Child Care Council (DVCCC) is a nonprofit organization dedicated to improving the quality, affordability, and accessibility of child care. A grant program from a private foundation enabled DVCCC and Gannett Fleming to develop a GIS project that maps public transit routes and child care center locations in the five-county Philadelphia region.

The GIS group at Gannett Fleming's Philadelphia office provided the DVCCC with professional cartography resulting in the production of a two-sided poster for distribution throughout the region.

More than 10,000 copies of the finished poster have been distributed and will eventually be displayed at every regional rail station, most nonprofit organizations, public social service organizations, and high schools. The poster is the first step in a strategy that provides better, more timely information to welfare caseworkers, enabling them to advise mothers seeking child care providers on the way to or within proximity of employment centers in the region.

North Carolina Public Health Response to Hurricane Floyd

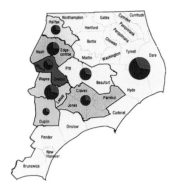

Reported Hospital Emergency Department Events Week of 9/16/99 - 9/22/99

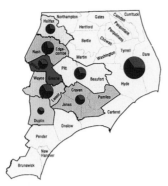

Reported Hospital Emergency Department Events Week of 9/30/99 - 10/6/99

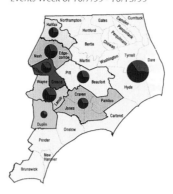

Reported Hospital Emergency Department Events Week of 10/7/99 - 10/13/99

Reported Hospital Emergency Department Events Week of 10/21/99 - 10/27/99

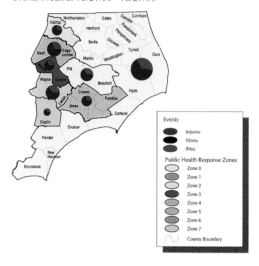

North Carolina Division of Public Health, Center for Health Informatics and Statistics
Raleigh, North Carolina

By Dianne Enright

Contact
Dianne Enright
dianne.enright@ncmail.net
Software
ArcInfo 7.2.1 and ArcView GIS 3.1
Hardware
Solaris 2.7
Printer
HP DesignJet 650C
Data Source(s)
North Carolina Division of Public Health, Epidemiology section
Map Type
Decision/Planning

In the weeks following the devastation of Hurricane Floyd, the North Carolina Division of Public Health conducted a surveillance of hospital emergency departments, before, during, and after the storm to determine the level of risk posed to people living in the eastern one-third of the state.

The 13 hardest hit counties were grouped into seven public health response zones to help with the organization and dissemination of information. The data sets were then reported geographically by zone each week. Emergency department events were grouped by illness (gastrointestinal), injury, and animal bites.

Water Testing in Flooded Areas Post Hurricane Floyd North Carolina

Water Sampling for Coliform

Water Sampling for *E. coli*

Swine Animal Operations 1999 Eastern North Carolina

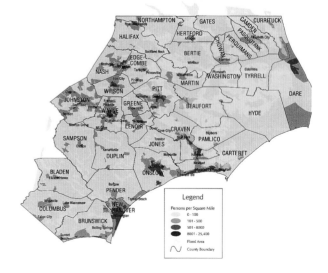

Household Overcrowding and Meningococcal Disease in Children

Proportion of Children Under 8 Years Old in Crowded Households per Census Area and Meningococcal Disease Cases (1995–1999)

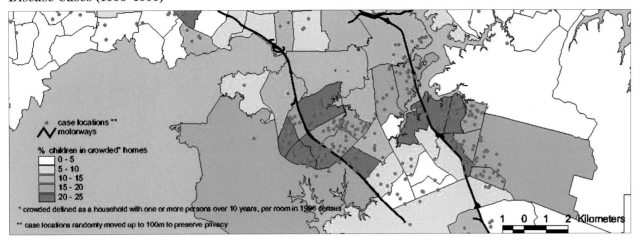

Number of Children Under 8 Years Old in Crowded Households and Meningococcal Disease Cases (1995–1999)

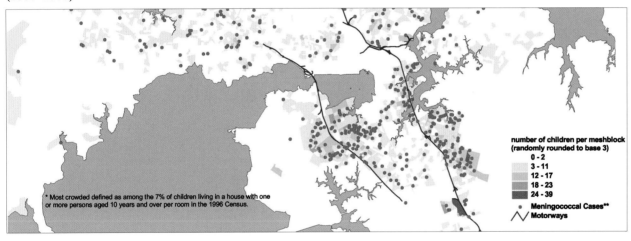

Auckland Public Health Protection
Auckland, New Zealand

By Dr. Nicholas Jones

Contact
Dr. Nicholas Jones
nickj@ahsl.co.nz
Software
ArcView GIS 3.1 and ArcPress
Hardware
Compaq DeskPro
Data Source(s)
Population data from Statistics New
Zealand, disease data from Auckland
Public Health Protection, and
boundaries and roads data from
Land Information New Zealand
Map Type
Inventory

During the last decade, New Zealand has experienced an epidemic of meningococcal disease, a severe bacterial infection causing meningitis or septicemia. Approximately 5 percent of cases are fatal. These maps are based on the findings of an epidemiological study done in Auckland. The study (Baker et al., Pediatric Infectious Disease Journal 2000; 19: 983–990) attempted to identify factors that increase the risk of children under eight years old catching meningococcal disease.

The most important factor was the ratio of people over 10 years of age per room in the child's house. In other words, children living in houses with several teenagers and adults, crowded into relatively few rooms, had a very high risk of catching this disease. The most likely reason for this finding is that adolescents and adults tend to be carriers for the bacterium.

The maps use census data to show the distribution of children at risk and physician reports to show the distribution of children with the disease.

The maps were used in a presentation to Housing New Zealand. This agency has since started a program to add more rooms to houses in areas where tenants have large families.

Epidemiology and GIS

Prince William County
Fire and Rescue
Prince William, Virginia

*By Dr. Jared Florence and
David J. Simms*

Contact
David Simms
dsimms@pwcgov.org
Software
ArcInfo 7.2.1 and ArcView GIS 3.1
Hardware
Windows NT
Printer
HP DesignJet 755CM
Data Source(s)
Prince William County Health
Department and Fire and Rescue GIS
Map Type
Modeling/Analytical

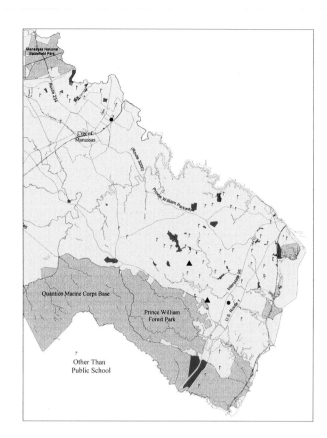

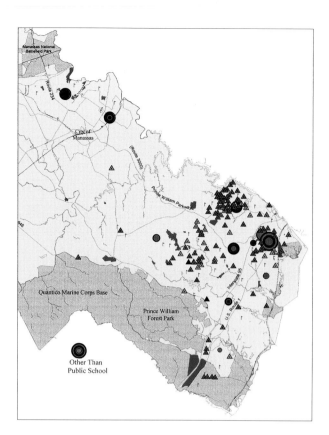

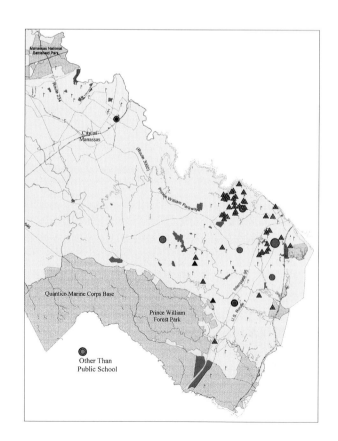

Epidemiology researchers can find clues to the spread of a disease as they study outbreaks of the disease through time, location, and groupings of people. In many cases, people with an illness belong to several groups such as family, school, church, and work. These groups are also identified by location. By mapping the location of various groups and looking at the presence of illness over time, it may be easier to identify the source of a disease and how it spreads. Knowing these factors can help doctors create a plan to halt the spread of disease.

The maps shown here depict the spread of measles through Prince William County in 1988. The locations of the patients by home address show a random pattern, while the plot by school shows obvious aggregations of cases. When viewed by two-week periods, the spread of the illness from school to school becomes apparent. In fact, during the outbreak it was possible to document dating patterns and sporting events that facilitated this spread. One of the control measures was halting certain sporting events.

Using additional GIS data layers, researchers can look for possible links to diseases by comparing disease clusters with extremely hazardous substance site (EHS) facilities and their vulnerability zones. In cases of illness for gastroenteritis, clusters can be viewed and possibly identified with restaurants and other commonly frequented establishments.

By implementing this analytical process with GIS, epidemiologists can identify, locate, and group illnesses with people, places, and activities; develop a plan; and initiate control measures to halt the spread of disease. This kind of process was used in handling the potential threat of the West Nile virus and the outbreak of human encephalitis, which began in New York City in early August 1999.

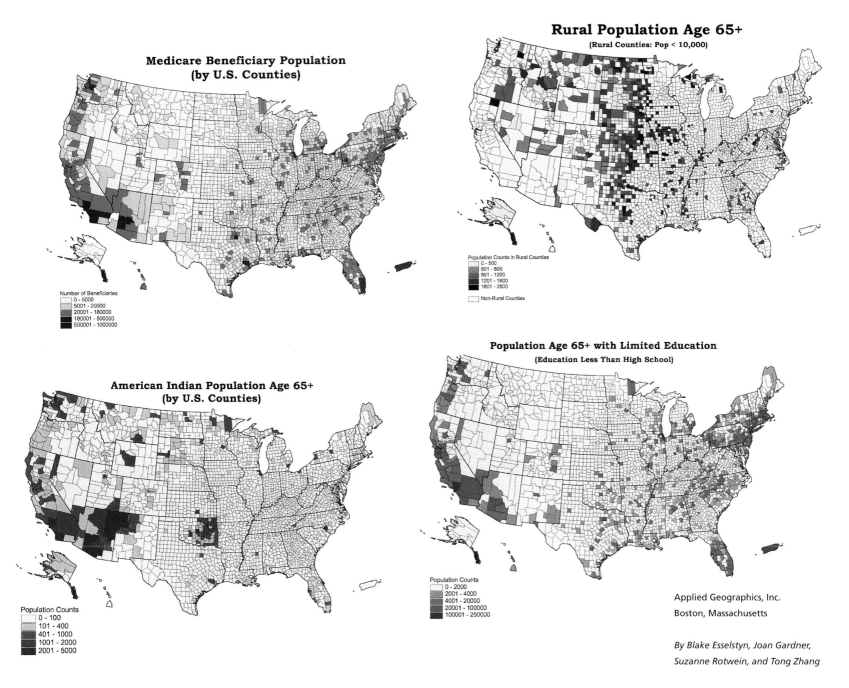

Medicare Beneficiary Population (by U.S. Counties)

Number of Beneficiaries
0 – 5000
5001 - 20000
20001 - 180000
180001 - 500000
500001 - 1000000

Rural Population Age 65+
(Rural Counties: Pop < 10,000)

Population Counts in Rural Counties
0 - 500
501 - 800
801 - 1200
1201 - 1600
1601 - 2500

Non-Rural Counties

American Indian Population Age 65+ (by U.S. Counties)

Population Counts
0 - 100
101 - 400
401 - 1000
1001 - 2000
2001 - 5000

Population Age 65+ with Limited Education
(Education Less Than High School)

Population Counts
0 - 2000
2001 - 4000
4001 - 20000
20001 - 100000
100001 - 250000

Applied Geographics, Inc.
Boston, Massachusetts

By Blake Esselstyn, Joan Gardner, Suzanne Rotwein, and Tong Zhang

The U.S. Health and Human Services Administration's Health Care Financing Administration (HCFA) Center for Beneficiary Services (CBS) is integrating GIS into an already well-developed social marketing initiative to better understand beneficiaries.

The project's objective was to identify, segment, and target HCFA beneficiaries so that HCFA's messages will be more relevant, focused, and better received by its beneficiaries. Applied Geographics, Inc.'s role was to identify relevant data sources for specific mapping requests, develop map templates, and map data by county to segment beneficiary populations.

Contact
Joan Gardner
jng@appgeo.com
Software
ArcView GIS
Hardware
Windows NT
Printer
HP
Data Source(s)
U.S. Census Bureau
Map Type
Inventory

ArcView GIS Mapping on CBS's *The District*

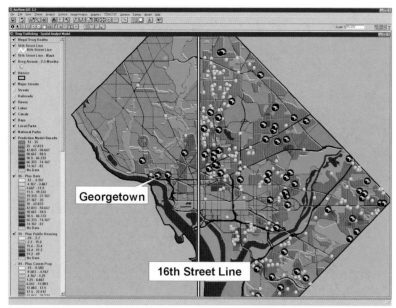

Using the ArcView Spatial Analyst and ModelBuilder™ technology, street-level drug trafficking areas are predicted by overlaying kids at risk, income, female-headed households, public housing projects, commercial properties, nuisance bars, and liquor stores.

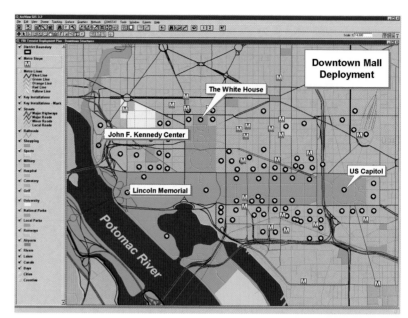

During a terrorist preparation activity, police are deployed at critical areas in the district including metro stops and key government facilities.

ESRI
Washington, D.C.

By John Calkins

Contact
John Calkins
jcalkins@esri.com
Software
ArcView GIS, ArcView Spatial
Analyst, ArcView 3D Analyst
Hardware
Compaq AP550 (Windows NT)
Printer
Digital only
Data Source(s)
Numerous
Map Type
Communication/Cartography

During the 2000–2001 television season, ESRI provided GIS support for CBS's police drama, *The District*. ArcView GIS is featured in each weekly episode as part of the comparative statistics (COMSTAT) process. Using a GIS, the police force is able to map crime throughout Washington, D.C., and solve a variety of problems.

The District, a drama inspired by the real-life experiences of former New York Deputy Police Commissioner Jack Maple, revolves around Jack Mannion (Craig T. Nelson), a tenacious champion of the underdog and avowed crime fighter, whose revolutionary tactics resulted in a 50 percent drop in crime, first in Boston, then in Newark, New Jersey.

When the controversial mayor of Washington, D.C., Ethan Baker (John Amos), needs to hire a new police chief, Deputy Mayor Jayne Brook (Mary Ann Mitchell) champions Mannion for the job, hoping the outsider can clean up the streets of her hometown. Washington, D.C., with more law enforcement agencies than any other city in the world, is riddled with crime, and its local police department is demoralized and ineffective.

Appointed chief of police by the mayor, Mannion is greeted with hostility, but with the help of his public relations whiz kid, Nick Pierce (Justin Theroux), sets out to revitalize the Metro force. Along the way, he recruits Ella Farmer (Lynne Thigpen), a hardworking statistics clerk and GIS specialist, and Temple Page (Sean Patrick Thomas), a young former Marine.

Ella is put in charge of a high-tech briefing room (COMSTAT) that uses ArcView GIS and ArcInfo. They tackle a variety of criminal and social problems, and Temple becomes Mannion's eyes and ears on the most crime-ridden, drug-infested streets in America. Danny McGregor (David O'Hara), a Royal Ulster Constabulary cop from Belfast, and Nancy Parras (Elizabeth Marvel), an intuitive officer working as Mannion's assistant, round out the chief's inner circle. Together, Mannion and his team form a modern-day "Untouchables," determined to make the district livable for all its citizens.

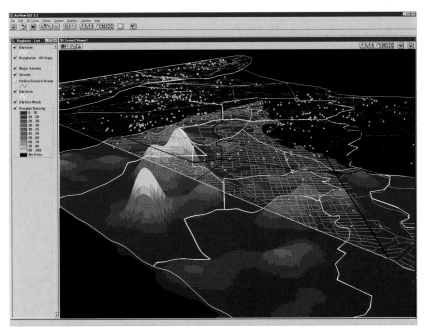

A hot spot (density surface) map of burglaries shows areas with the greatest concentration. ArcView 3D Analyst portrays the results after the surface is created with ArcView Spatial Analyst.

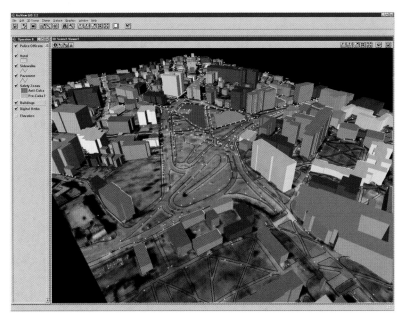

Three-dimensional visualization helps analyze the police deployment pattern necessary to protect a visiting dignitary and the anticipated protesters.

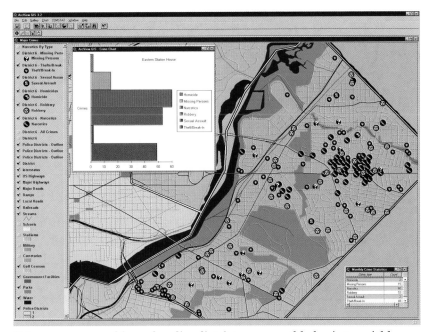

Crimes are mapped in each police district on a monthly basis to quickly identify patterns and problems.

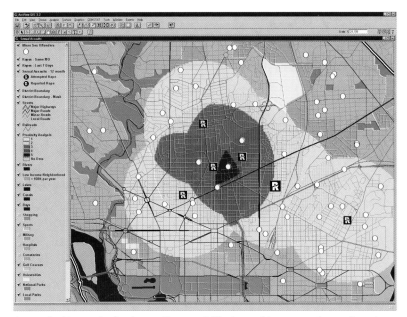

A proximity analysis shows the most likely residence or place of work of a serial rapist. ArcView Spatial Analyst calculates neighborhood statistics using the average distance between incidents.

Flood Insurance Policy Locations

PREFERRED RISK RATE
ALL OTHER FLOOD INSURANCES
AR FLOOD HAZARD ZONE BOUNDARY
PARCELS IN THE AR FLOOD HAZARD ZONE

City of Lakewood
Lakewood, California

By Michael Jenkins

Contact
Sonia Southwell
ssouthwe@lakewoodcity.org
Software
ArcInfo 7.2.1, ArcPress 2, and
ArcView GIS 3.1
Hardware
HP 9000/735 series workstation and
Gateway Pentium II PC
Printer
HP DesignJet 650C
Data Source(s)
Various
Map Type
Inventory

In 1998, the Federal Emergency Management Agency designated a portion of the city of Lakewood to be within a 100-year floodplain or special flood hazard area (SFHA). At that time, property owners within the SFHA were given a limited time opportunity to purchase flood insurance at a discounted or preferred policy rate. All insurance policies purchased after the deadline were at the standard insurance rate.

The Flood Insurance Policy Locations map shows where flood insurance policies were purchased in relation to the location of the SFHA and demonstrates the effectiveness of the flood zone education campaign promoted by the city of Lakewood. Most of the insurance policies purchased were within the SFHA. Approximately 70 percent of those policies were purchased before the effective date of the flood map and at the discounted or preferred policy rate, which saved individual property owners hundreds of dollars in insurance premiums.

City of Phoenix General Plan

City of Phoenix
Phoenix, Arizona

By Kelly Walker

Contact
Kelly Walker
kwalker1@ci.phoenix.az.us
Software
ArcInfo 7.2
Hardware
UNIX
Printer
HP DesignJet 755CM
Data Source(s)
General Plan in Corel Draw
Map Type
Decision/Planning

General Plan Categories

Hatched Mixed Use categories designates a mixture of uses corresponding to the colors shown.

- 1 dwelling unit / acre or less
- 0 to 2 dwelling units / acre
- 0 to 2 with a cap of 1.2 du/acre
- 0 to 2 with a cap of 1.5 du/acre
- 2 to 5 dwelling units / acre
- 2 to 5 with a cap of 2.5 du/acre
- 2 to 5 with a cap of 3.5 du/acre
- 5 to 10 dwelling units / acre
- 5 to 15 dwelling units / acre
- 10 to 15 dwelling units / acre
- 10+ dwelling units / acre
- 15+ dwelling units / acre
- Transition from Industrial to Residential
- Industrial
- Commerce Park
- Commercial
- Desert Preserve
- ♥ Proposed Park in Area
- ♪ Proposed School in Area
- ® Resort
- Density Cap
- Private Recreation

- Mixed Use (Area C and D only)
  A Specific Plan is required before project approval.
- Mixed Use Agriculture
- Mixed Use (See NOTES #1 below)
- Mixed Use Commercial / Commerce Park
- Mixed Use Commercial / Residential 2-5
- Mixed Use Commercial / Residential 5-15
- Conservation Community
- Nurseries / Flower Gardens
- Parks / Open Space
- Hillside
- Public / Quasi-Public
- Floodplain
- Undesignated
- ─·─·─ Canal, Watercourse
- ─··─·· Wash Corridor
- ─── Transportation
- ─ ─ ─ Future Transportation
- · · · · Infrastructure Limit Line (North Black Canyon)
- ▨▨ Transportation Corridor
- ✳ Primary Core
- ✳ Secondary Core
- ····· Existing Railroad

This map represents a vision for the future of Phoenix. It shows a portion of the 476 square miles of the city, along with a proposed street network.

The General Plan was previously prepared using Corel Draw software. To provide more precision and to enable area calculations and housing density projections to be computed, the General Plan was re-researched and a coverage was created using ARCEDIT. Because this map was to be sent to a printer, ARC Macro Language was used to produce the final product so that the PostScript file color codes would be CMYK instead of RGB.

New Berlin GIS Maps

Planning Department Counter Map

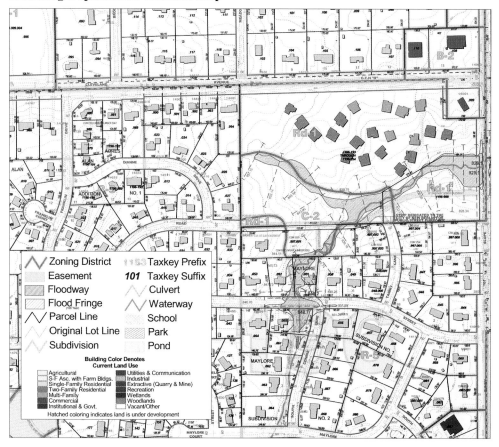

Aldermanic Districts

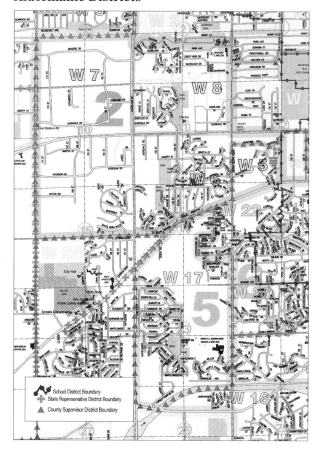

City of New Berlin
New Berlin, Wisconsin

By David B. Haines

Contact
David Haines
dhaines@newberlin.org
Software
ArcView GIS 3.2
Hardware
Windows Intel
Printer
HP DesignJet 1055CM
Data Source(s)
City of New Berlin Planning,
Engineer, and Assessor departments;
Waukesha County Register of Deeds
Land Information Services;
Southeastern Wisconsin Regional
Planning Commission; and Federal
Emergency Management Agency
Map Type
Automation and Communication/
Cartography

Planning Department Counter Map

The New Berlin Planning Department uses the counter map as its general information map. It provides information such as property lines and dimensions, road rights-of-way, buildings, structures, road edge location, drainage culverts, lot numbers, subdivision name, tax identification keys, easements, street addresses, zoning, land use, floodplain location and elevation, and site grading. It explains the spatial component of the city, county, state, and federal land use regulations to citizens, landowners, and developers. It consists of 78 themes in three different views, which were generated and modified by ArcInfo. It is updated yearly.

Aldermanic Districts

In New Berlin, a polling place may serve more than one voting district. The voter rolls are kept separate by ward, and there are different voting stations at a polling place for each ward that is represented. Because this can create confusion among citizens, voters use a map to quickly determine the voting ward in which they reside. Created after the 1990 redistrict, those maps were old and worn.

The city wanted new "Know Your Ward" maps but did not want to spend much time on them with Census 2000 redistricting around the corner. The Land Information Services Division made new, attractive maps within one week. To show the aldermanic (city council) ward, school, state representative, and county supervisor districts all on one map, the same color was selected for aldermanic districts, and inside buffers were used to create the thick ward outlines. The "points-along-a-line" Avenue™ script created the boundary for the school, state representatives, and county supervisor districts.

Total Property Values (Private Property)

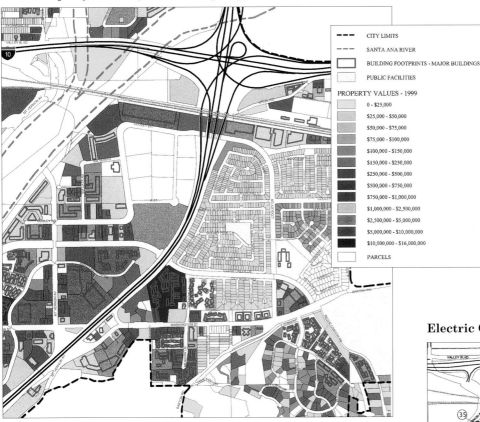

– – –	CITY LIMITS
– – –	SANTA ANA RIVER
☐	BUILDING FOOTPRINTS - MAJOR BUILDINGS
☐	PUBLIC FACILITIES

PROPERTY VALUES - 1999

- 0 - $25,000
- $25,000 - $50,000
- $50,000 - $75,000
- $75,000 - $100,000
- $100,000 - $150,000
- $150,000 - $250,000
- $250,000 - $500,000
- $500,000 - $750,000
- $750,000 - $1,000,000
- $1,000,000 - $2,500,000
- $2,500,000 - $5,000,000
- $5,000,000 - $10,000,000
- $10,000,000 - $16,000,000
- PARCELS

City of Colton
Colton, California

By Rick Whitaker

Contact
Rick Whitaker
rwhitaker@ci.colton.ca.us
Software
ArcView GIS 3.2
Hardware
Windows NT
Printer
HP DesignJet 750C+
Data Source(s)
County parcels, Metroscan database, Colton orthophotography, Colton rights-of-way, and electric circuit data
Map Type
Inventory

Total Property Values

This map was created using the parcel layer as the base map. Other themes used were the public facilities parcels from the zoning theme and the building footprints theme. The latest Metroscan data was joined to the parcels theme using the assessor's parcel number field, and then data in the total property value field was classified as shown in the legend.

Electric Circuits Map

The city street rights-of-way theme served as the base layer for this map. An AutoCAD drawing, created from the original 12-kilovolt Mylar circuit map for the electric utility, was converted into ArcInfo coverages and then to shapefiles.

The result has three essential components—electric circuit, switches, and substations. Lines were classified for the circuit layer by circuit name and whether they are overhead or underground circuits. For the switch layer, the points were classified into switch location and underground open connections. The substation point layer was classified by substation name.

Electric Circuits Map

SWITCHES AND OPEN CONNECTORS
- ● SWITCH
- ○ OPEN CONNECTOR (CUTOUTS, JUMPERS, ELBOWS)
- ☐ SUB STATION

LINE DESIGNATIONS
- – – – OVERHEAD LINES
- ——— UNDERGROUND LINES

HUB SUBSTATION CIRCUITS
- CONGRESS
- LA CADENA
- LA LOMA
- LAUREL
- MT VERNON
- RANCHO
- SPERRY

- VALLEY

DREWS SUBSTATION CIRCUITS
- HOSPITAL 1
- HOSPITAL 2
- RIVERSIDE
- SLOVER

CENTURY SUBSTATION CIRCUITS
- BARTON
- COOLEY
- MOHAVE
- RECHE CANYON
- SANTA ANA
- WASHINGTON
- – – – CITY LIMITS
- ——— SANTA ANA RIVER

Affordable Housing Assessment

City of Encinitas, GIS Division
Encinitas, California

By Frank McDermott III and
Amanda Mills

Contact
Frank M. McDermott III
fmcdermo@ci.encinitas.ca.us
Software
ArcInfo and ArcView GIS
Hardware
Windows NT
Printer
HP650C
Data Source(s)
City of Encinitas, San Diego
Association of Governments,
SanGIS, and U.S. Census Bureau
Map Type
Decision/Planning

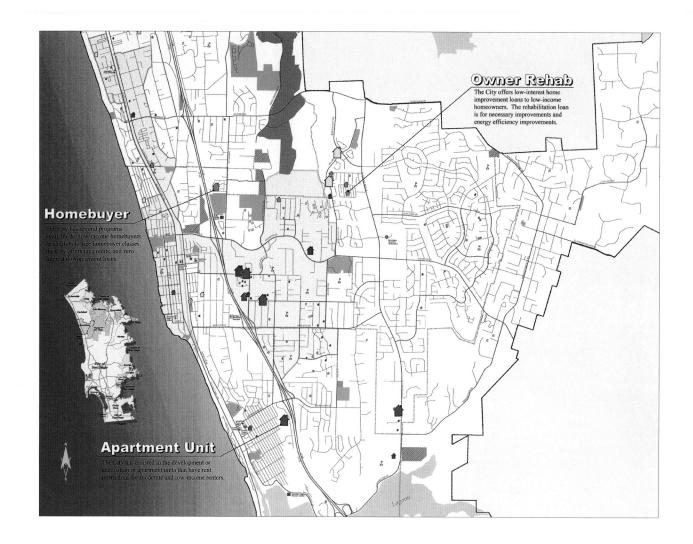

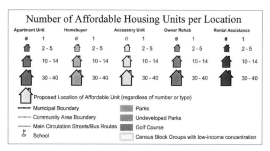

Primarily built out and seeking potential affordable housing projects, the city of Encinitas is looking for acquisition opportunities in underdeveloped lots appropriate for rehabilitation or new construction.

The city developed this Affordable Housing Assessment map to address questions about which areas were appropriate for multifamily affordable housing in the city, whether the city was meeting the need for affordable housing in low-income areas, if there was too much affordable housing, and where the city should look to develop additional affordable housing opportunities.

Considering the density, proximity to services, and presence of low-income households, the city determined that the greatest opportunity for affordable housing development would be within the communities of Leucadia and Cardiff. After the completion of this assessment, the city of Encinitas began work in conjunction with the San Diego Chapter of Habitat for Humanity to build seven new single-family homes for low-income families in neighboring Leucadia.

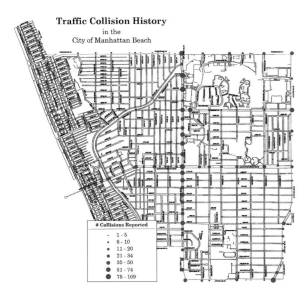

Traffic Collision History
in the
City of Manhattan Beach

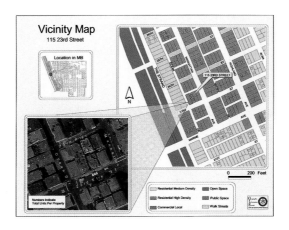

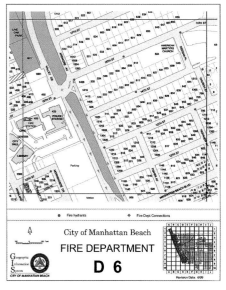

Downtown Manhattan Beach
Commercial Business Types

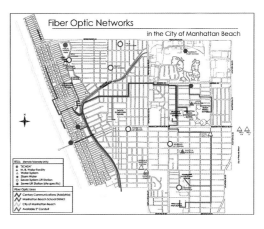

This display highlights some of the varied maps produced by the city of Manhattan Beach GIS division. Although technically a part of the public works department, the GIS division serves the needs of the entire city. The fire department, for example, uses a series of run maps, which depict hydrant locations, one-way streets, and dead-end streets, to respond to calls more safely and efficiently. The police department also uses GIS maps to make neighborhood and site-specific analyses of crime and traffic patterns. And, with the assistance of vicinity maps, the city council and planning commission can visualize the projects they are evaluating.

Infrastructure project maps and Underground Utility maps not only organize and categorize, but also give a "big picture" look at the many planned and ongoing public works projects. Maps with features such as fiber-optic networks, cultural sites, and city-owned land are invaluable for inventorying the city's rich and varied resources.

In addition to these maps, the GIS division also produced a Fault Zone map providing city building officials with an at-a-glance guide for determining earthquake-related building codes, an Election map for the City Clerk's office, and a Facility Information map for the city's newsletter.

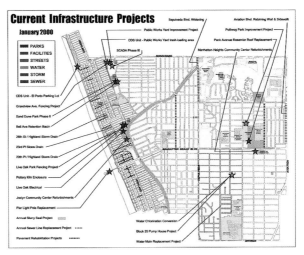

City of Manhattan Beach
Manhattan Beach, California

*By Don Boudreau and
Bonnie Shrewsbury*

Contact
Bonnie Shrewsbury
bshrewsbury@ci.manhattan-beach.ca.us
Software
ArcInfo 7.2.1 and ArcView GIS 3
Hardware
Windows 98 and Windows NT
Printer
HP DesignJet 2500CP PS3
Data Source(s)
Various
Map Type
Automation

Missouri City GIS Maps

City of Missouri City Residential Subdivision Map

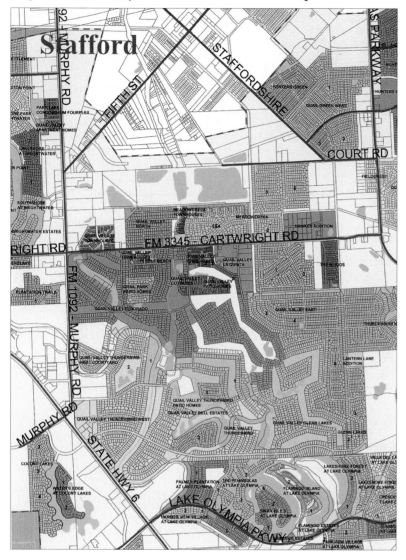

City of Missouri City Drug Free Zones

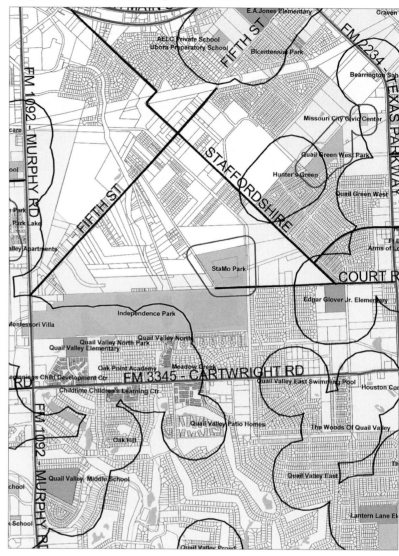

City of Missouri City
Missouri City, Texas

By Mark Hochstein

Contact

Mark Hochstein

mhochstein@ci.sugar-land.tx.us

Software

ArcInfo

Hardware

Windows NT

Printer

HP DesignJet 3000CP

Data Source(s)

City of Missouri City

Map Type

Decision/Planning

All city departments use the Missouri City Residential Subdivision map, which was created using the city's GIS parcel coverage and tax database. With ArcInfo, subdivision numbers were selected from within the parcel coverage data and then dissolved to create the new coverage. Minor cleanup was performed to finalize the coverage.

The Drug Free Zone map has enabled the Missouri City Police Department to put a little more bite into local drug law enforcement. The buffered areas on the map created in ArcView GIS are zones where drug violations carry a double penalty.

The idea to create this map came from a neighboring city's police and engineering departments. That city manually created a similar type of map at a cost of several employees' man-hours during a one-month period. In less than eight man-hours, one Missouri City employee using ArcView GIS, existing GIS coverages, and Texas data acquired free via the Internet created an improved map.

Illustrative Map of Downtown Grand Rapids, Michigan

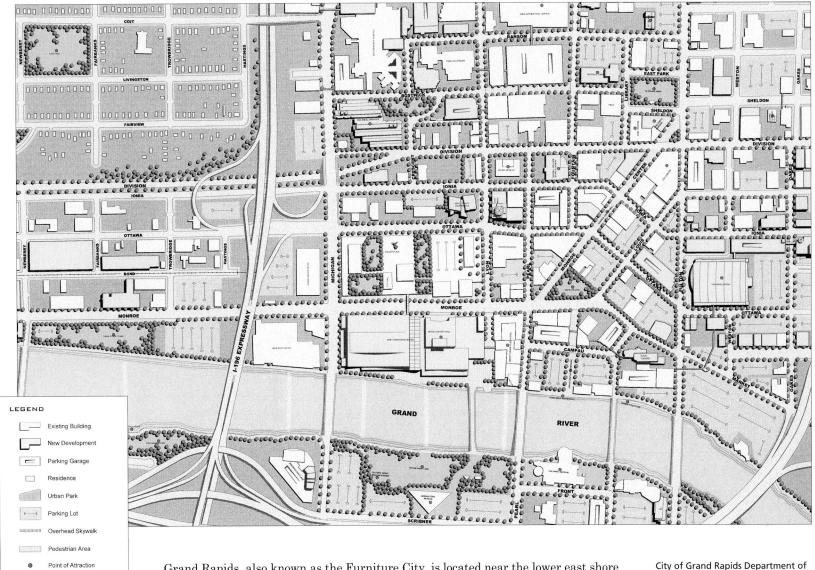

LEGEND

	Existing Building
	New Development
	Parking Garage
	Residence
	Urban Park
	Parking Lot
	Overhead Skywalk
	Pedestrian Area
●	Point of Attraction
	Railroad

Grand Rapids, also known as the Furniture City, is located near the lower east shore of Lake Michigan. Ranked by *Fortune Magazine* as one of the top 10 best cities for business in the United States, the city recently has experienced rapid economic growth, especially in the downtown area. This map illustrates new developments, prominent buildings, pedestrian walkways, green spaces, and tourist attractions, as well as existing structures and urban streetscape. It helps city planners, decision makers, developers, and the public to visualize current conditions and envision future opportunities for the downtown. Various public and private organizations use it as a base map.

Creating this illustrative map required a high level of spatial accuracy, detailing (e.g., building roof lines, sky walks, landscape), color rendering (e.g., buildings, blocks, pavements, river, trees), and three-dimensional effects (e.g., shadow casting, multilevel roadway intertwining). These graphic treatments greatly enhance the reality and aesthetics of the map. ArcView GIS, AutoCAD, and ArcInfo facilitated this complex illustrative mapping process. This map is an excellent example of the application of GIS software for illustrative urban design and cartography.

City of Grand Rapids Department of Information Technology
Grand Rapids, Michigan

By Yuli Siao

Contact
Yuli Siao
ysiao@ci.grand-rapids.mi.us

Software
ArcInfo 7.1, ArcView GIS 3.1, and AutoCAD 14
Hardware
Windows NT
Printer
HP DesignJet 750C+
Data Source(s)
Downtown Grand Rapids base maps
Map Type
Communication/Cartography

Fairfax County Fire and Rescue Department—1996 Activity

Activity with Seven-Minute Coverage

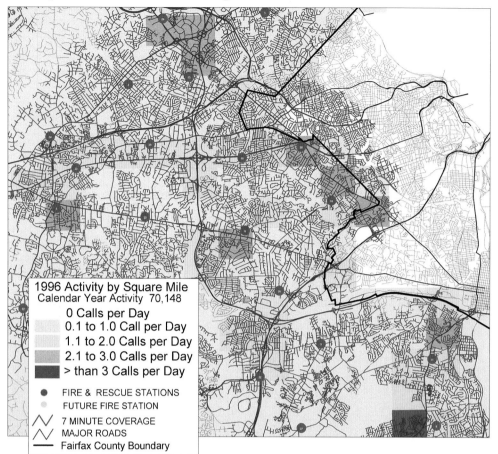

1996 Activity by Square Mile
Calendar Year Activity 70,148
- 0 Calls per Day
- 0.1 to 1.0 Call per Day
- 1.1 to 2.0 Calls per Day
- 2.1 to 3.0 Calls per Day
- > than 3 Calls per Day
- ● FIRE & RESCUE STATIONS
- ○ FUTURE FIRE STATION
- 〜 7 MINUTE COVERAGE
- 〜 MAJOR ROADS
- — Fairfax County Boundary

Activity by Station First Due Area

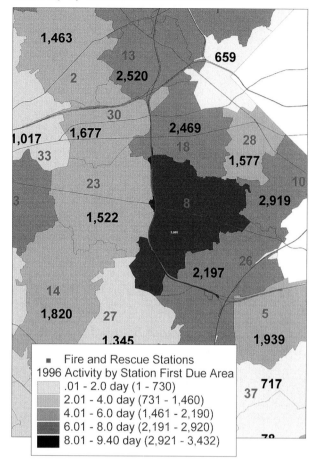

■ Fire and Rescue Stations
1996 Activity by Station First Due Area
- .01 - 2.0 day (1 - 730)
- 2.01 - 4.0 day (731 - 1,460)
- 4.01 - 6.0 day (1,461 - 2,190)
- 6.01 - 8.0 day (2,191 - 2,920)
- 8.01 - 9.40 day (2,921 - 3,432)

Fairfax County Fire and Rescue
Department, Systems Management
Section
County of Fairfax
Fairfax, Virginia

*By Ralph Dulaney and
Laurie Shertzer*

Contact
Eric Fisher
eric.fisher@co.fairfax.va.us
Software
ArcView GIS 3.2
Hardware
Dell Optiplex GX1P
Printer
HP DesignJet 650C
Data Source(s)
Fairfax County, Virginia
Map Type
Decision/Planning

Activity with Seven-Minute Coverage

This multivariant map depicts three main data themes—the seven-minute travel time coverage area that radiated outward from each existing fire station, a thematic coverage that displays the average number of calls per day per square mile, and the proposed locations of future fire stations.

Used in a relocation study, this map helped to determine existing high-risk areas that might require additional fire stations. The map was also used by the Fairfax County Fire and Rescue Department, citizens, and the County's Board of Supervisors to show the locations of fire stations, travel times, and areas of different average activity in evaluating the county's response goal—to provide effective fire suppression and emergency medical services.

Activity by Station First Due Area

This thematic map depicts 1996 emergency incident activity by fire station first due area. In Fairfax County, first due areas are where a single fire station has primary responsibility. In this map, first due areas are color coded by the average number of incidents per day. In addition, the total number of incidents for the year are labeled in each first due area.

By showing the locations of the fire stations and their respective first due areas, this map helped to evaluate the variation in workload between stations and summarize activity for the Fairfax County Fire and Rescue Department, citizens, and the County's Board of Supervisors.

Fairfax County Department of
Information Technology, GIS and
Mapping Services Branch
County of Fairfax
Fairfax, Virginia

*By Fairfax County GIS and Mapping
Services Branch*

Contact
Eric Fisher
eric.fisher@co.fairfax.va.us
Software
ArcInfo 8.0.1
Hardware
IBM RISC/6000 and Dell Precision 610
Printer
HP DesignJet 3500CP
Data Source(s)
Fairfax County, Virginia
Map Type
Automation

An example of the new standard Fairfax County Cadastral map, this one illustrates the use of more than 30 layers of data, symbology, and annotation and is the result of Fairfax County's multiyear effort to convert its existing hard-copy parcel maps into a digital GIS format.

Since 1970, the county's 400 square miles of land had been divided into a map tile system of 444 sheets and mapped at 1:2,400 scale. The data conversion began in 1997 when the county's ink-on-Mylar maps depicted more than 320,000 individual parcels. The resulting digital data now resides in an ArcSDE database that is available to county users enterprisewide.

Building and Construction Patterns in Honolulu

City and County of Honolulu
Honolulu, Hawaii

By Jon Hodge, Mark Lierman,
Ken Schmidt, and Lisa Wurlitzer

Contact
Ken Schmidt
kschmidt@pixi.com
Software
ArcInfo
Hardware
UNIX
Printer
HP DesignJet 3500CP
Data Source(s)
Honolulu Land Information System
Map Type
Automation

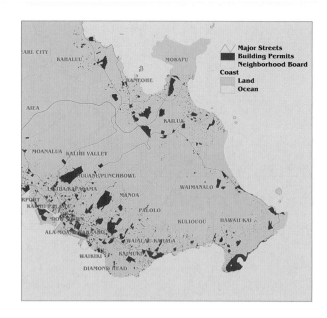

The city and county of Honolulu deployed a new permitting system to improve the methods and processes for approval of construction and development permit applications. The conversion and integration of disparate permit records into a comprehensive database of regulatory and land information has significantly expanded the abilities of city engineers, architects, and planners to monitor construction patterns throughout the island of Oahu.

Direct links between the GIS and the POSSE system enable spatial access of permit applications and records. The city's GIS program enables direct display of permit data and information, and the GIS data maintenance operations updates subdivision and land control records directly into the permit database.

These maps illustrate the permit data details that can be displayed according to their geographic locations. Patterns of permits issued can be studied to determine the impacts of their distributions. The GIS automatically assigns permit inspections and determines human resource allocations. The system supports mission-critical programs, and it is designing and planning better methods to manage, track, and enforce construction activities.

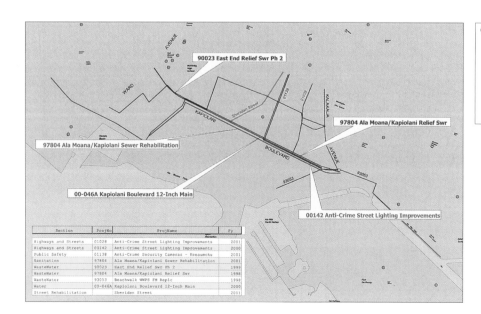

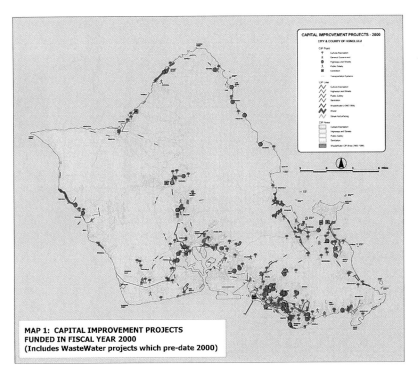

MAP 1: CAPITAL IMPROVEMENT PROJECTS
FUNDED IN FISCAL YEAR 2000
(Includes WasteWater projects which pre-date 2000)

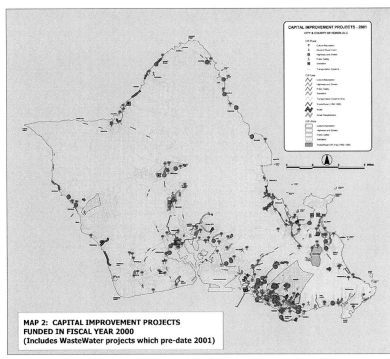

MAP 2: CAPITAL IMPROVEMENT PROJECTS
FUNDED IN FISCAL YEAR 2000
(Includes WasteWater projects which pre-date 2001)

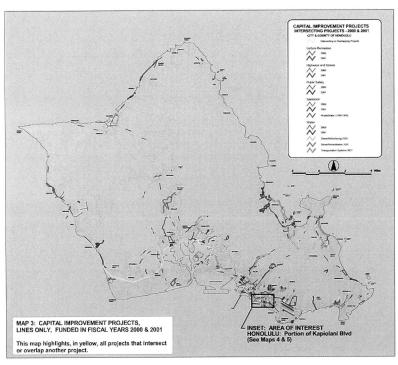

MAP 3: CAPITAL IMPROVEMENT PROJECTS,
LINES ONLY, FUNDED IN FISCAL YEARS 2000 & 2001

This map highlights, in yellow, all projects that intersect
or overlap another project.

INSET: AREA OF INTEREST
HONOLULU: Portion of Kapiolani Blvd
(See Maps 4 & 5)

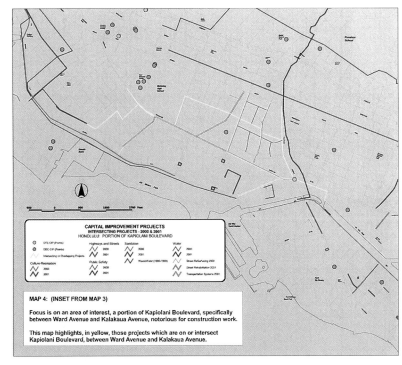

MAP 4: (INSET FROM MAP 3)

Focus is on an area of interest, a portion of Kapiolani Boulevard, specifically
between Ward Avenue and Kalakaua Avenue, notorious for construction work.

This map highlights, in yellow, those projects which are on or intersect
Kapiolani Boulevard, between Ward Avenue and Kalakaua Avenue.

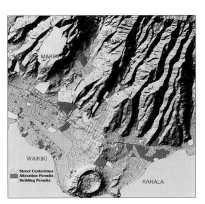

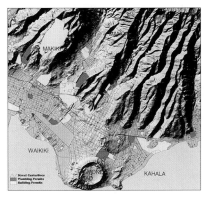

Urban Resources Management and Environmental Monitoring Via GIS Software Technologies

Municipality of Galati
Galati, Romania

By Viorel Mancas

Contact
Viorel Mancas
viorel_m@primaria.galati.ro
Software
ArcInfo 7.2.1, ARC TIN, ArcView
GIS 3.2, and ArcView 3D Analyst
Hardware
Digital Alpha 433au
Printer
HP DesignJet 1055CM
Data Source(s)
1:5,000-scale elevation, hydrography,
planimetry, and utilities network
maps
Map Type
Decision/Planning

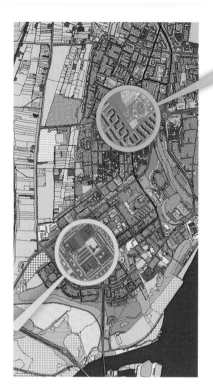

Galati, a city of about 400,000 located on the Danube River, represents one of the major urban areas in Romania that is slated for development. The implementation of GIS technology for urban resource management is helping to provide sensible urban development and environmental protection for Galati. Thematic maps and data attributes include parcel units, basic land use, buildings, roads, railways, and parks. This data is accessible to users and supports local government operations such as tax assessment, public transportation, garbage collection, street lighting, and traffic signage.

Because the town is surrounded by water, a digital terrain model (DTM), which covers a surface of more than 5,878 hectares, will be used to identify areas at risk for floods, erosion, and an increase of the phreatic layer.

Maps created with ArcView 3D Analyst by overlapping the DTM with several themes are also useful in the development process of the city. The implementation of GIS technology for urban resource management is helping to provide sensible urban development and environmental protection for Galati.

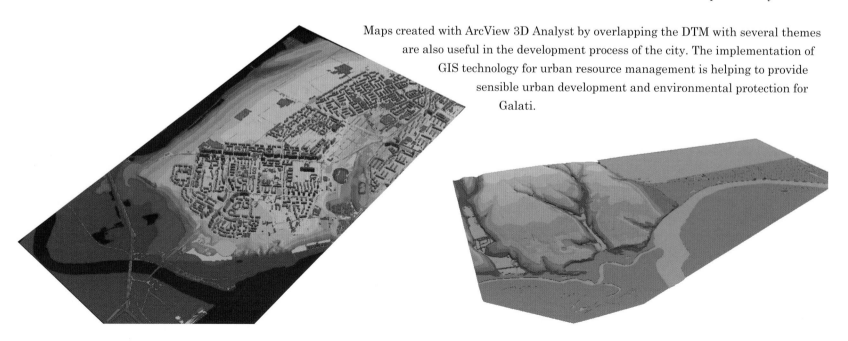

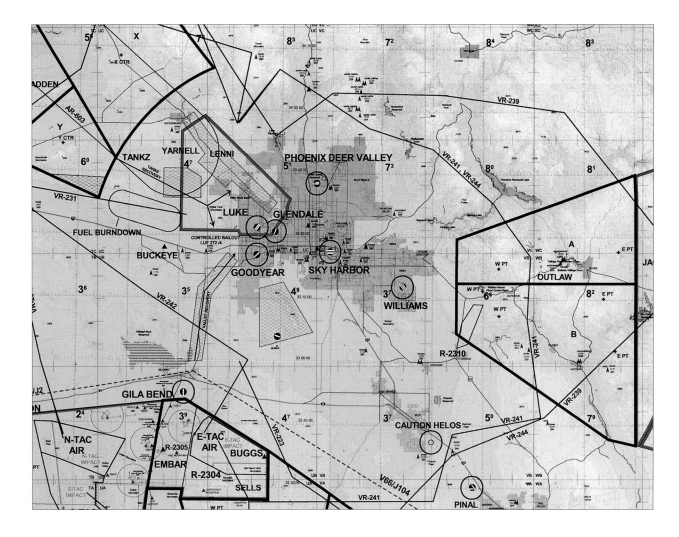

Instructional pilots use the Tactical Pilotage Chart as a supplemental tool during training of F-16 student pilots at Luke Air Force Base near Phoenix, Arizona. The chart contains surface and airspace data, such as elevation, major roads and cities, airfields, obstructing towers and cables, training routes, restricted airspace, no-fly areas, communication points, tactical areas, and other military operating areas, covering Arizona.

The Standards and Evaluations Group, an education component of the 56th Operations Group at Luke Air Force Base, commissioned the chart. More than 100 of these charts are circulating among the fighter squadrons attached to Luke Air Force Base and several divisions of the 56th Range Management Office.

56th Range Management Office
Luke Air Force Base, Arizona

By BTG, Inc., Applied Engineering Services and Luke Air Force Base, 56th Range Management

Contact
Cory Brose
cbrose@hushmail.com
Software
ArcInfo 8 and ArcView GIS 3.2
Hardware
Windows NT
Printer
HP DesignJet 3000
Data Source(s)
U.S. Department of Defense flight information publication and Luke Air Force Base 56th Fighter Wing
Map Type
Communication/Cartography

Navy Site Planning—Recruit Training Command Great Lakes

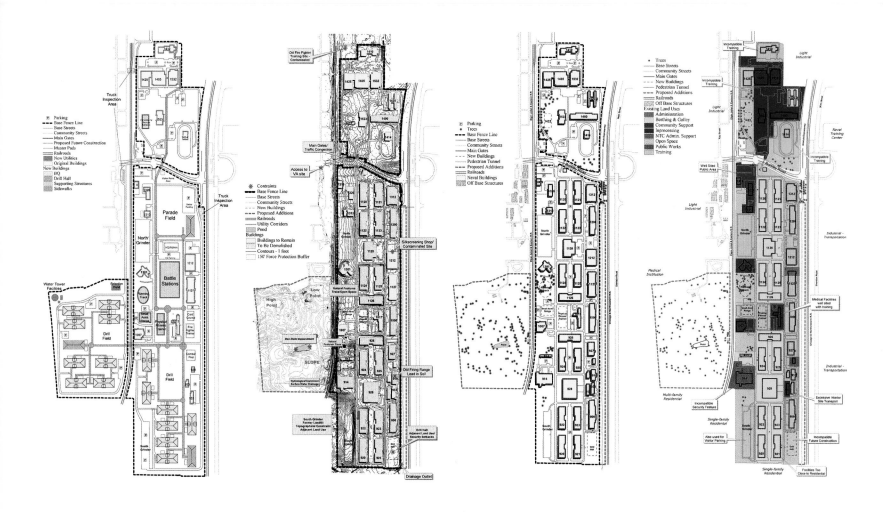

U.S. Navy
Charleston, South Carolina

By Todd Horton

Contact

Marc Batten, Todd Horton, and
Brian VanBockern

hortonjt@efdsouth.navfac.navy.mil

Software

ArcView GIS 3.2a

Hardware

Dell Pentium III

Printer

HP DesignJet 750C

Data Source(s)

In-house production and Chief of
Naval Education and Training
Facilities/Environmental GIS database

Map Type

Decision/Planning

This map is part of a series used in the analysis of the possible site redevelopment at the U.S. Naval Recruit Training Command (RTC) Great Lakes located in northeastern Illinois. The installation houses approximately 54,000 recruits each year. The barracks are overcrowded and need to be replaced because the facilities are out-of-date, the structures are deteriorating, and there is insufficient utility capacity.

RTC Great Lakes requested a site analysis of the installation to prepare proposed site redevelopment plans illustrating environmentally sound solutions for improving and managing the land and facilities while supporting the RTC mission. Several planning guidelines were set such as the creation of a campus environment, segregation of vehicles from recruit pedestrian traffic, incorporation of antiterrorism/force protection setbacks, minimizing negative impacts to the adjacent community, and consolidation of common land use functions into activity corridors.

In addition to the design criteria, planners were required to maintain a constant berthing capacity for 16,000 recruits, minimize the adverse impacts to recruit training activity, and maximize the use of existing infrastructure. To help in this process, the maps identified proposed functional districts and land use zones within the RTC; utility corridors; facility/building locations; natural resource features; and transportation, vehicular, and pedestrian circulation modes.

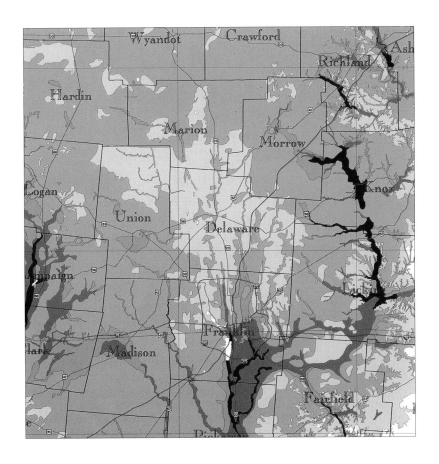 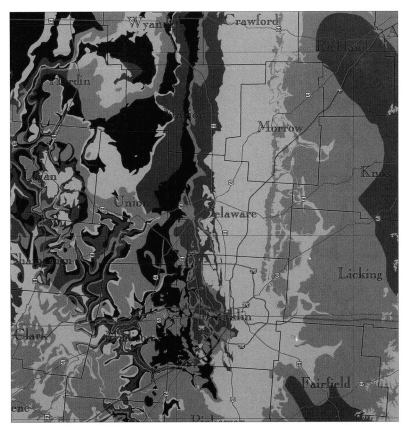

The Ohio Department of Natural Resources, Division of Water, has produced statewide GIS coverages for the unconsolidated and bedrock aquifers of Ohio. These maps depict the approximate yield, in gallons per minute, of the aquifers. Lighter colors represent lower yields, and darker colors represent higher yields.

Well logs, drilling reports, and other geologic and hydrogeologic information were used to delineate the unconsolidated and bedrock aquifer maps. These hand-drawn, 7.5-minute quadrangle maps (1:24,000) were digitized and joined to produce statewide polygon coverages. In addition to yield, attributes for the bedrock aquifer coverages include aquifer extent, name, and thickness. Additional attributes for the unconsolidated aquifers include drift thickness, hydrogeologic settings, local names, and lithology.

Before it had created the GIS coverages, the Division of Water produced countywide groundwater resource maps at a 1:62,500 scale. The county maps were produced using traditional cartographic and printing methods, which made correcting and updating a difficult and expensive process. The new statewide GIS maps provide more information at a higher level of detail than the existing county maps while seamlessly incorporating updates into the process. Now, consultants, engineers, planners, homeowners, and well drilling contractors, who are interested in developing a groundwater supply, have current and accurate information on the groundwater resources of Ohio.

These maps were funded, in part, by a grant from the Ohio Environmental Protection Agency under provisions of Section 319 of the Clean Water Act.

Ohio Department of Natural Resources, Division of Water, Hydrogeology Program Columbus, Ohio

By Michael Angle, Frank Fugitt, Bill Haiker, Michael Hallfrisch, Wayne Jones, Darlene Magold, Ken Pendley, Paul Spahr, and Kathy Sprowls

Contact
Paul Spahr
paul.spahr@dnr.state.oh.us
Software
ArcInfo 7.2.1, ArcPress, and ArcView GIS 3.1
Hardware
UNIX and Windows NT workstations
Printer
HP DesignJet 755CM
Data Source(s)
Various geologic and hydrogeologic publications, maps, reports, test well data, well logs, and drilling reports
Map Type
Automation

Water Resource Management—Stream Flow, Salmon Restoration, and Water Allocation

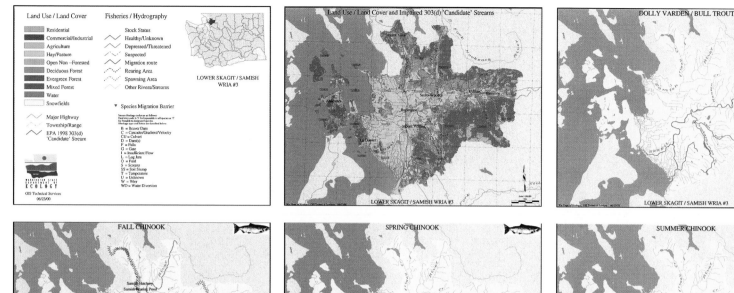

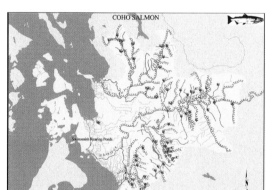

Washington Department of Ecology,
GIS Technical Services Group
Olympia, Washington

By Mike Woodall

Contact
Joy Denkers
jden461@ecy.wa.gov

Software
ArcInfo 7.2 and ArcPress

Hardware
Sun Ultra 60 workstation

Printer
HP DesignJet 650C

Data Source(s)
Washington Department of Ecology, Washington Department of Natural Resources, Washington Department of Fish and Wildlife, Washington Office of Financial Management, and U.S. Geological Survey

Map Type
Communication/Cartography

This map series was designed to show the extent and status of anadromous fish in streams within Water Resource Inventory areas of Washington. The maps were produced using ArcInfo, ARCPLOT, and dynamic segmentation against a 1:100,000-scale stream network spatial database. The anadromous fish data sets are compiled in event tables (SASI, rearing, and spawning) or point coverages (barriers, facilities) produced by the Washington State Department of Fish and Wildlife.

Each Salmonid map shows the status of a species of anadromous fish within the stream network of a Water Resource Inventory area. Additional land use/land cover information, EPA 303(d) listed streams, and township/range section data are provided for identifying areas of development, pollution, and water-right adjudication.

The report, along with the maps and data, was submitted and used in support of a pending lawsuit on water quantity metering and to illustrate fish management within watershed planning areas.

Decadal Development Within the Las Vegas Valley, Nevada, from the Year 1950 through 1999

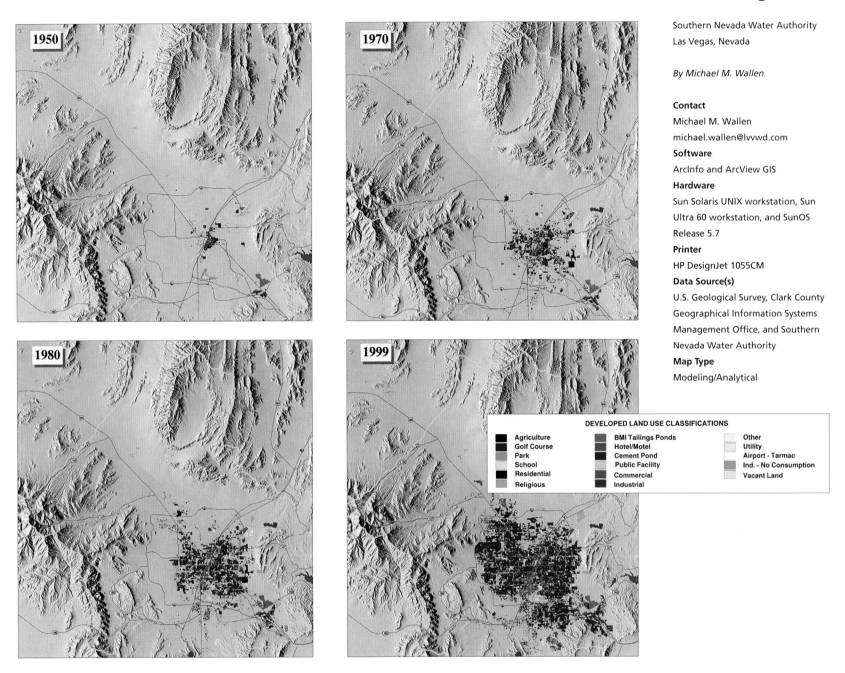

Southern Nevada Water Authority
Las Vegas, Nevada

By Michael M. Wallen

Contact
Michael M. Wallen
michael.wallen@lvvwd.com
Software
ArcInfo and ArcView GIS
Hardware
Sun Solaris UNIX workstation, Sun Ultra 60 workstation, and SunOS Release 5.7
Printer
HP DesignJet 1055CM
Data Source(s)
U.S. Geological Survey, Clark County Geographical Information Systems Management Office, and Southern Nevada Water Authority
Map Type
Modeling/Analytical

DEVELOPED LAND USE CLASSIFICATIONS

Agriculture	BMI Tailings Ponds	Other
Golf Course	Hotel/Motel	Utility
Park	Cement Pond	Airport - Tarmac
School	Public Facility	Ind. - No Consumption
Residential	Commercial	Vacant Land
Religious	Industrial	

The Southern Nevada Water Authority (SNWA) Ground Water Management Program uses MODFLOW for analysis of secondary recharge. Because of the dynamic growth within the Las Vegas valley, historical development grids were generated.

As a base, the Clark County Assessor's Office maintains coverages and a database of more than 400,000 parcels within Clark County. One item within the database is "construction year," which served as an excellent resource for developing the grids. The "construction year" item only records the year of current development, and there were many properties built in the 1950s and 1960s that were demolished and replaced with new types of development in the 1980s and 1990s.

To fill in the gaps and locate missing development, data sets from satellite imagery, historical aerial photography, U.S. Geological Survey 7.5-minute quadrangles, historical maps, and the historical record were used. This produced an eye-opening representation of what has been happening in the valley during the last 50 years.

Vegetation Communities in the Flinders Ranges

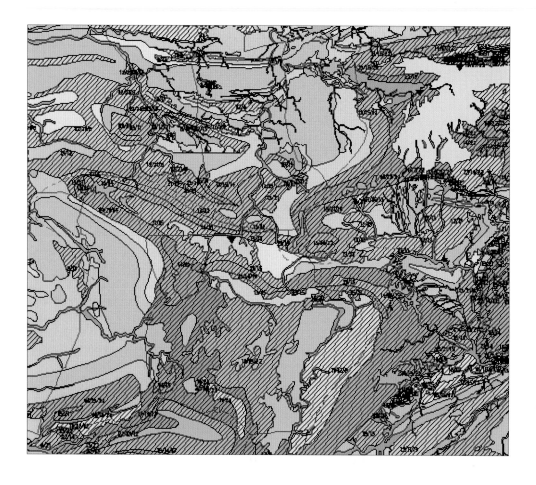

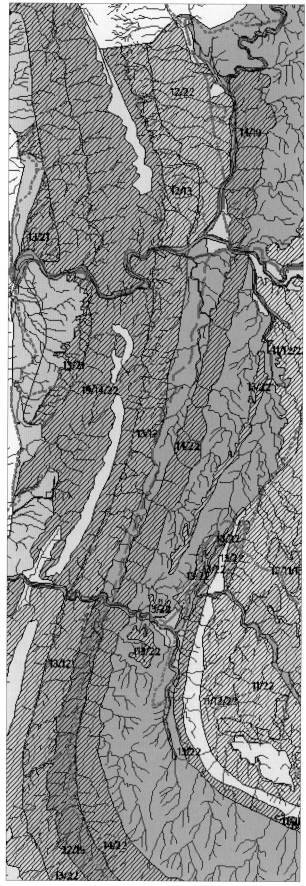

Department of Environment and
Heritage
Adelaide, South Australia, Australia

By Tim Hudspith

Contact
Tim Hudspith
hudspith.tim@saugov.sa.gov.au

Software
ArcInfo 7.2.1
Hardware
Sun SPARC 2 E4000 workstation
Printer
HP DesignJet 750C
Data Source(s)
Landsat Thematic Mapper satellite
imagery and aerial photography
Map Type
Inventory

These maps show the distribution and extent of native vegetation communities in the Flinders Ranges Region of South Australia and are part of the Biological Survey of South Australia. The Flinders Ranges is a geologically ancient and complex system of steep rugged ranges, high plateaus, gorges, and wide open valleys.

The natural beauty of the region makes it a popular destination for artists, photographers, and nature lovers. The climate varies from Mediterranean in the south, where cool wet winters are followed by warm dry summers, to arid in the north, where rainfall is rare and summer temperatures often exceed 40 degrees C. The region incorporates a number of national parks.

Minerals Management Service Automation for the Spatial Assessment of Hydrocarbon Resources

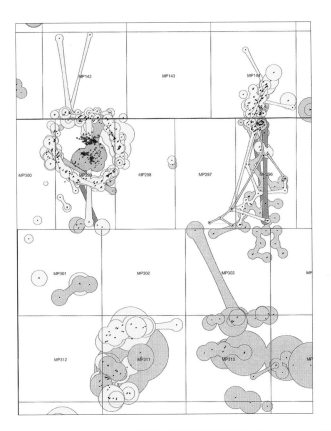

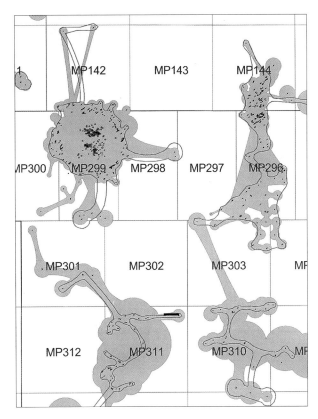

U.S. Department of the Interior, Minerals Management Service (MMS) New Orleans, Louisiana

By Michele Aurand, Michele Daigle, Kewen Huang, and Paul Rasmus

Contact
Michele Aurand
wendy.villere@acs-gsg.com

Software
ArcView GIS 3.1, ArcSDE 3.0.2, SDE® C API, and Oracle 7.3.4
Hardware
Windows 98 and Sun Solaris
Printer
HP DesignJet 650C and HP DesignJet 755CM
Data Source(s)
MMS publicly releasable well, geological, and paleological data
Map Type
Automation

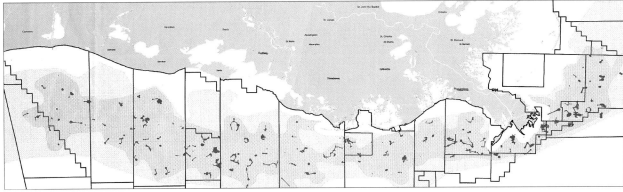

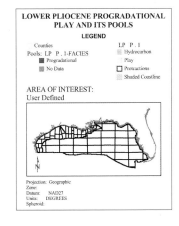

In 1999, the Minerals Management Service (MMS) released to the public a CD–ROM of the Assessment of Conventionally Recoverable Hydrocarbon Resources of the Gulf of Mexico and Atlantic Outer Continental Shelf as of January 1, 1995. Polygon outlines for pools, fields, and plays were included as shapefiles on the disk. Faced with a rise of in-house requests for access to spatial data and pressure to meet a deadline for a fall 2000 release of the Assessment as of January 1, 1998, the Information Technology Office (ITD) and Resource Evaluation Office concentrated their efforts on automating the creation of spatial features for reservoirs, sands, pools, and plays.

A customized ArcView GIS extension helps users load and query reservoir, sand, pool, and field polygons. By examining a single field at a time, MMS users have been able to ascertain where well completions or reservoirs might be assigned to the wrong field or where the location of a completion is incorrect in the corporate database. In addition to having regularly updated in-house Spatial Database Engine™ (SDE) layers, MMS can also generate static slice-in-time shapefiles for the assessment CD–ROM, where the rule of release for public information is that the data must be at least two years old.

Sardis Lake Bathymetric Survey

Oklahoma Water Resources Board
Oklahoma City, Oklahoma

By Kevin Koon and Michael Sughru

Contact
Michael Sughru
mpsughru@owrb.state.ok.us

Software
ArcInfo 7.x, ArcView GIS 3.1,
ArcView Spatial Analyst,
and ArcView 3D Analyst
Hardware
Windows NT
Printer
HP DesignJet 3500CP
Data Source(s)
Oklahoma Water Resources Board
and U.S. Geological Survey
Map Type
Communication/Cartography

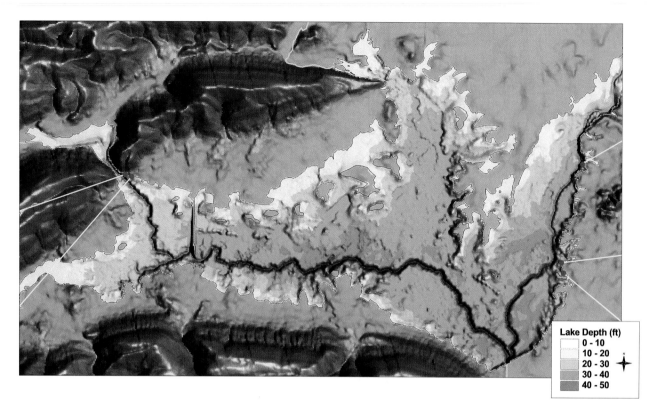

The Oklahoma Water Resources Board developed a comprehensive GIS database of the Kiamichi River Basin, which includes digital layers of lakes, rivers, streams, groundwater aquifers, soils, land use, environmentally sensitive areas, endangered species, digital elevation models, digital orthophotography, permitted groundwater and stream water locations, cities, and roads.

To determine the total available water in the basin, the water board conducted bathymetric mapping of Hugo and Sardis lakes, which provided valuable information regarding the depths and volumes of the lakes. The GIS has helped the Water Resources Board demonstrate how seasonal fluctuations in lake levels will affect the surrounding parks and resource areas. Using digital elevation models, the board could determine the volumes and areas of proposed lakes and show how they would look.

The Water Resources Board used GIS technology for more than 30 presentations about this project. The power of GIS enables the public to see and easily understand the information presented helping them in the process of resolving the issues.

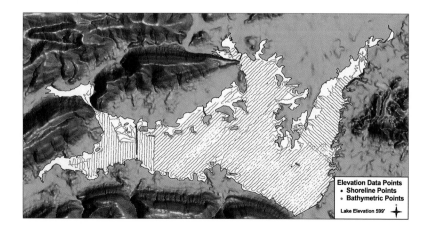

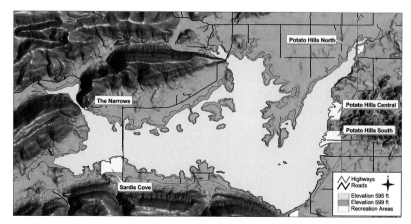

An 'In-Depth' Look at Northern California Bathymetry

California Resources Agency,
Department of Fish and Game
Sacramento, California

By Will Patterson

Contact
Will Patterson
wpatters@dfg.ca.gov
Software
ArcInfo 7.2.1 and 8, ArcView GIS 3.2,
ArcView 3D Analyst 1, and ArcView
Spatial Analyst 2
Hardware
Windows NT and Sun 300 server
Printer
HP DesignJet 1055CM
Data Source(s)
National Ocean Service, Teale Data
Center, United States Geological
Survey
Map Type
Communication/Cartography

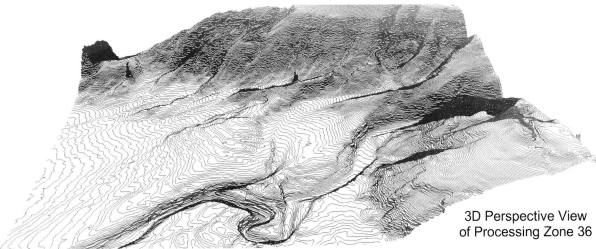

3D Perspective View
of Processing Zone 36

In a cooperative effort between the Teale Data Center GIS Solutions Group and the California Department of Fish and Game, bathymetric data sets from various sources were gridded, contoured, and then plotted using ESRI software.

Among the contributing data sets, some six million National Ocean Service Hydrographic Survey depth points were processed for the entire California coast. Due to the volume of input data, processing was performed in 100-kilometer-by-100-kilometer zones. The ArcInfo commands TopoGrid and LatticeContour were used as primary interpolation algorithms. ArcInfo and ArcView GIS facilitated the checkplots and data visualization.

In Northern California, especially dense hydrographic survey data provided excellent near shore detail for the gridding and contouring processes. This poster, produced using ArcView GIS 3.2, ArcView Spatial Analyst 2, and ArcView 3D Analyst 1, illustrates some of the spatial data now available to assist with marine resources research and management.

Spatial Analysis of Bottom Habitats and Sand Deposits on the Continental Shelf off South Carolina

South Carolina Department of
Natural Resources, Marine Resources
Division
Charleston, South Carolina

By Philip Weinbach

Contact

Philip Weinbach

weinbachp@mrd.dnr.state.sc.us

Software

ArcView GIS 3.1 and ArcView Spatial
Analyst

Hardware

Windows NT

Printer

HP DesignJet 1055CM

Data Source(s)

Minerals Management Service
INTERMAR database

Map Type

Modeling/Analytical

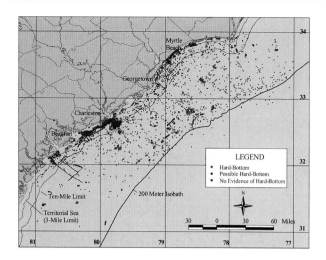

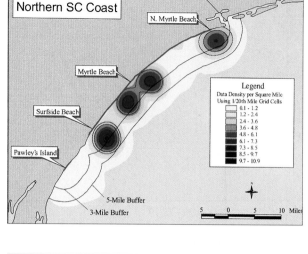

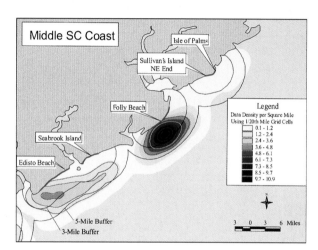

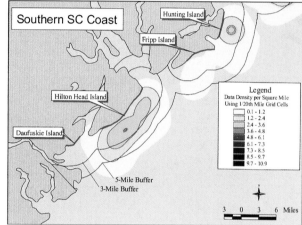

In July 1992, South Carolina entered a cooperative agreement with the Minerals Management Service (MMS). This program evaluates the sand, mineral, and hard bottom resources that exist on the coastal shelf. During the first year, an interagency Task Force on Offshore Resources reviewed and summarized the historical information available for the South Carolina coastal zone. Continued efforts produced the extensive database used to create this map.

The major parameters investigated were mean size, sediment thickness, percent sand, and hard bottom locations. Using the database to locate appropriate mining sites was difficult in some areas because of data gaps. Another emphasis of this project was to locate these data gaps, which would supply spatial information to future data acquisition efforts.

South Carolina's coastline is a very popular residential area and tourist destination. Unfortunately, many of these areas are eroding. This project plays a vital role in ensuring that the resources necessary for nourishment projects are located, which will provide protection for these valuable economic and ecological treasures.

Petroleum Exploration in New Zealand—Basin Modeling Using GIS

EXAMPLE INPUT GRIDS

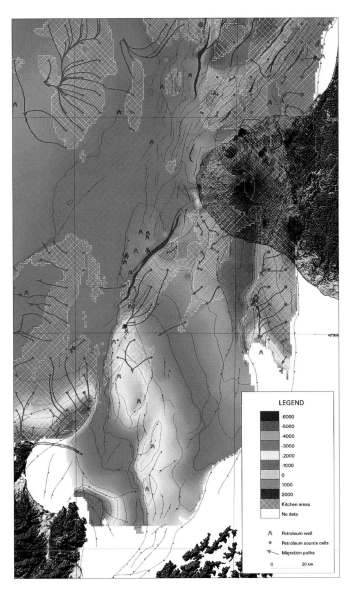

Isopachs

Pliocene Extension

TOC
(Source Rock Richness)

Time grids

Paleobathymetry

Institute of Geological and
Nuclear Sciences
Lower Hutt, New Zealand

By Gael Cutress, Rob Funnell, Phil
Scadden, and Ray Wood

Contact
Phil Scadden
p.scadden@gns.cri.nz
Software
ArcInfo 7.1.2
Hardware
Sun workstation
Printer
HP DesignJet 1055
Data Source(s)
In-house
Map Type
Modeling/Analytical

LEGEND
-6000
-5000
-4000
-3000
-2000
-1000
0
1000
2000
Kitchen areas
No data

Petroleum well
Petroleum source cells
Migration paths

0   20 km

The evolution of New Zealand's sedimentary basins has been complex, often involving radical changes in tectonic history and depositional styles. The structural complexity of New Zealand's basins makes exploration for oil and gas particularly difficult.

This project presents a multiple one-dimensional modeling approach developed by the Institute of Geological and Nuclear Sciences, which investigates the relationships between basin evolution and the formation and migration of hydrocarbons.

The technique combines a one-dimensional basin modeling program and ArcInfo to present map-based maturity and structural data for anytime in the basin's history. ArcInfo software's hydrologic functions trace the flow directions of oil generated from mature "kitchens" using present day or paleostructure migration horizons.

The display shows the entire petroleum system including migration paths, structural development, and the distribution of mature sources and potential reservoirs. More complex migration algorithms are being developed. The oil industry has reacted to initial presentations with considerable interest.

OUTPUT GRIDS

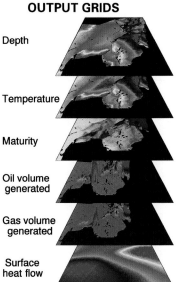

Depth

Temperature

Maturity

Oil volume generated

Gas volume generated

Surface heat flow

Oil Exploration Maps

Offshore Brazil Planning Map

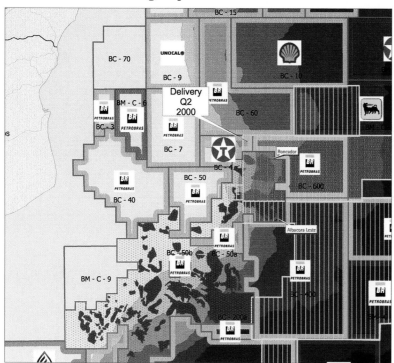

Mississippi Canyon Project—Salt Thickness

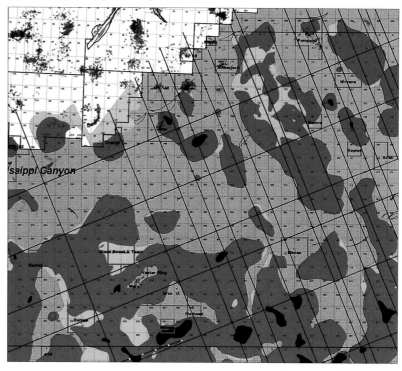

PGS Exploration
Houston, Texas

By Robert L. Arbo

Contact
Robert Arbo
robert.arbo@pgs.com

Software
ArcView GIS 3.2, ArcView Spatial
Analyst 1.1, Adobe Photoshop, and
Microsoft Excel (Offshore Brazil);
ArcView GIS 3, Viewpoint Document
Manager, and Viewpoint TurboMap
(Mississippi Canyon)

Hardware
Windows NT

Printer
HP DesignJet 1050C

Data Source(s)
Public domain data from the
Internet and PGS proprietary data
(Offshore Brazil); PGS proprietary
data, Minerals Management Service,
and Lexco Data Systems (Mississippi
Canyon)

Map Type
Automation, Communication/
Cartography, and Decision/Planning

Offshore Brazil Planning Map

This map shows the locations and status of PGS surveys as well as the location and leasing status of the Brazilian offshore concession blocks. This reference is used throughout PGS companies and divisions to plan future surveys and show the weekly and daily status of survey completions. Along with the Gulf of Mexico lease operator's maps, it has also become an important marketing tool to show PGS involvement in the Campos, Santos, and Portiguar basins off the coast of Brazil.

The survey boundaries were derived from actual navigation GPS coordinates taken from seismic vessels. The bathymetry grid was enhanced in some places by using seismic bin center depths. Using GIS for this map not only provided a pleasing visual product for marketing, but its accurate area calculations are useful in planning and survey design.

Mississippi Canyon Project—Salt Thickness

One of several plates designed for a specific study in the northern Gulf of Mexico Mississippi Canyon area, this project was commissioned to study a particular focus area and gather as much information as possible for a detailed report. The report was for sale as a research tool, and it was a value-added addition to a seismic data package for oil companies interested in possible drill sites or reservoir evaluations for that area.

The challenge in making this map came from trying to integrate research essays and thesis works into a workable GIS coverage. It involved a complicated process of delineating hundreds of salt polygons from paper reports and accurately portraying them on a map. This plate came from collaborations with several geologists, geophysicists, and GIS specialists.

Water System Shutdown Drainage Analysis Using Elevation Data

ELEVATION

SHADED RELIEF AND CONTOURS

MODELED STREAM NETWORK

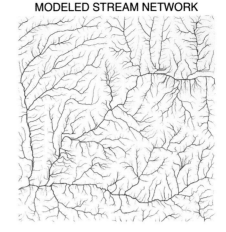

PIPELINE SLOPE

OVERLAY

IMAGERY

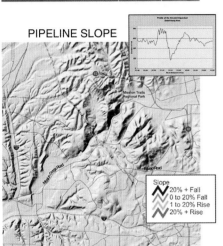

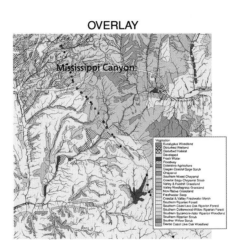

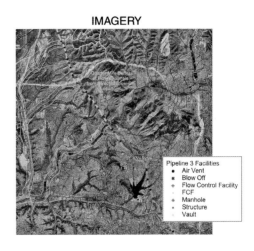

The San Diego County Water Authority GIS Department developed a mapping and analysis tool to assess potential impacts on property and the environment during system shutdowns. The ARC Macro Language application produces several data layers that can be displayed and analyzed in ArcView GIS.

The San Diego County Water Authority supplies 90 percent of the county's water through more than 272 miles of major pipelines and other water facilities. The authority provides both treated and raw water to its 23 member agencies, which deliver that water for ultimate consumption. The system is composed of two aqueducts that contain five major pipelines ranging from 48 inches to 114 inches in diameter. The water flows by gravity from north to south and is regulated at Lake Skinner in Riverside County.

To provide a safe and reliable supply of water, periodic shutdowns of the system are necessary to accommodate new pipeline connections, perform routine maintenance, and assess the condition of the existing system. After the flow of water is stopped at the source, the pipeline is drained in the locations where work is scheduled. Shutdowns are typically scheduled in the winter when water demands are low and can last from 10 days to several months, depending on the work.

A pipeline shutdown requires intense coordination between departments at the authority including rights-of-way, operations and maintenance, environmental, and public affairs. In addition, coordination with member agencies is critical to ensure that adequate water supplies are available during the shutdown. This tool is used before the shutdown operation to determine the potential drainage impacts and to notify affected property owners.

San Diego County Water Authority
San Diego, California

By Laura Edwards, Dan Hildebrand, and Fred Wong

Contact
Fred Wong
fwong@sdcwa.org
Software
ArcInfo and ArcView GIS
Hardware
Windows NT
Printer
HP DesignJet 3500CP
Data Source(s)
10-meter digital elevation model, facility surveys, U.S. Geological Survey digital orthoquarter quadrangles, and San Diego Association of Governments regional data
Map Type
Modeling/Analytical

Eurasia Pipelines of the 21st Century—Preliminary Design of Oil and Gas Pipelines for Feasibility Study Based on GIS Technology and Remote Sensing Data

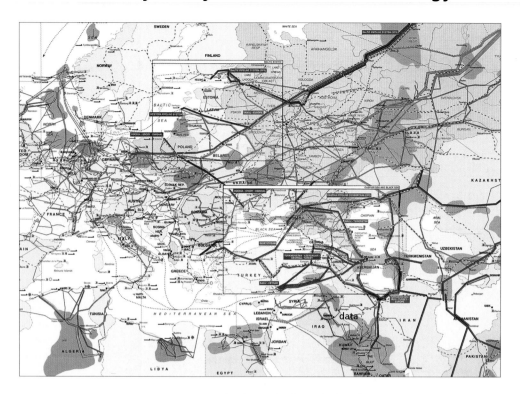

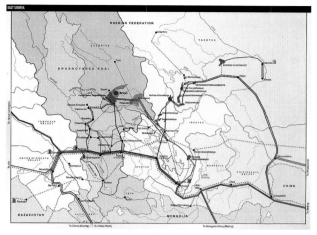

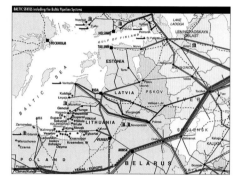

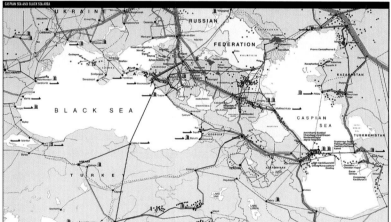

Petroleum Economist/RNGS–
Engineering
Moscow, Russia

By Ivan Mazur, RAO/RNGS

Contact
Leonid Vedechine
lvedeshin@mail.ru
Software
ArcInfo
Hardware
Pentium V
Printer
CalComp ColorJet
Data Source(s)
Russian Academy of Sciences
Map Type
Communication/Cartography

Based on modern computer technology for designing pipeline systems, this map shows 12 different routes of oil and gas pipelines from 20 gas and oil fields from eastern Siberia to Beijing.

Derived from aerospace data, GIS, and intelligence systems, the 12 routes were assessed technically and economically and include calculation of investments, payback periods, and oil and gas rates at the point of intersection with the Chinese border. This technology uses patented solutions for designing virtual images of selected pipelines.

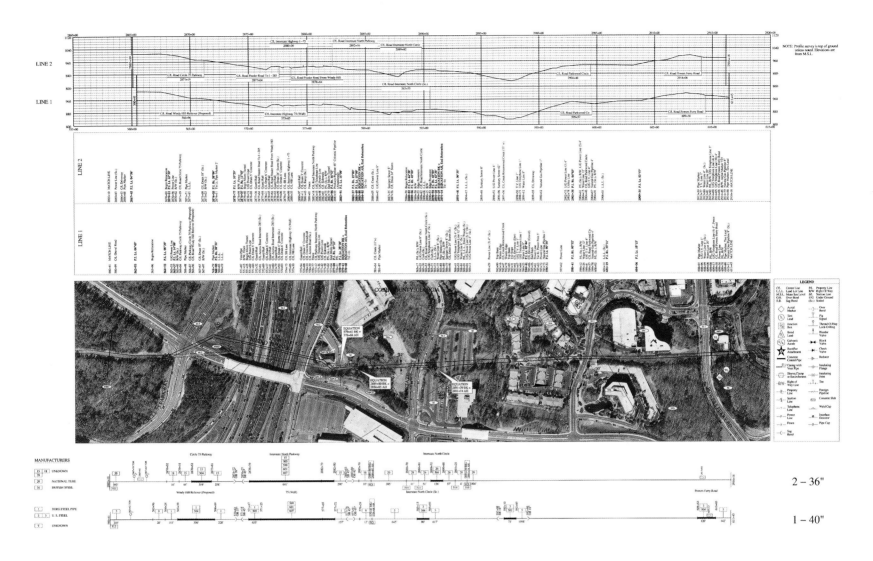

GeoFields, Inc.

Colonial Pipeline Company (CPC)

Atlanta, Georgia

By Roger Eldridge, Jimmy Gambrell, Mike Pielow, and Craig Tomlinson

Contact

Eric James

ejames@geofields.com

Software

ArcInfo 8

Hardware

Windows NT

Printer

HP DesignJet 1055CM

Data Source(s)

CPC

Map Type

Automation

Colonial Pipeline Company (CPC) is an interstate common carrier of petroleum products. The 5,307-mile Colonial system transports fuel from Texas, Louisiana, Mississippi, and Alabama refineries to 267 marketing terminals located near major population centers along the southeast and east U.S. coasts.

GeoFields has collected and processed data for the entire CPC system including aerial photography, facility data, rights-of-way data, and land base layers. The GeoFields Alignment Sheet Generator for ArcInfo uses the data to create automated, large-scale alignment sheet drawings. The application has produced nearly 2,000 alignment sheet drawings, which are typically at a 1:400 or 1:200 scale and can be easily updated, maintained, and distributed. Alignment sheet generation is just one component of the CPC enterprise GIS program, which includes data management, new project support, risk assessment, Web-based data delivery, and emergency response support. CPC is creating a spatial database of its entire system.

Alternative Corridor View-Shed Analysis

Photo Science, Inc.
Tucker, Georgia

By Christopher Smith

Contact
Christopher Smith
cdsmith@photoscience.com
Software
ArcInfo 8, ArcPress, ArcView GIS 3.2,
and ArcView 3D Analyst
Hardware
Windows NT
Printer
HP DesignJet 755CM
Data Source(s)
Orthophotography; U.S. Geological
Survey; and Rabun County, Georgia,
Tax Assessor maps
Map Type
Decision/Planning

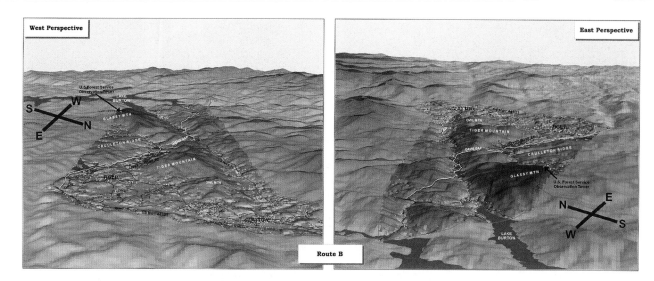

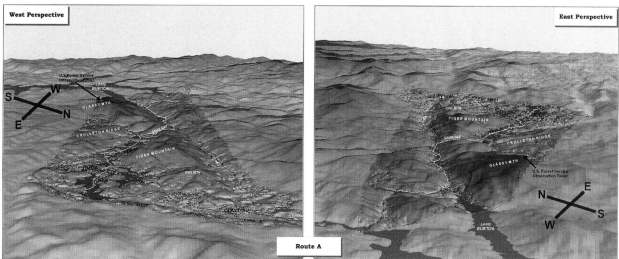

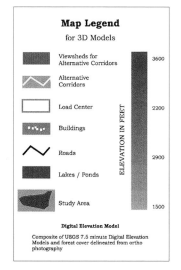

The information on this map, along with other graphics and materials, was presented at a public meeting. The map shows view sheds for alternative transmission line corridors.

View sheds were created with ArcView 3D Analyst, and a digital elevation model (DEM) used for the process was generated from a mosaic of U.S. Geological Survey 7.5-minute DEMs with the addition of a general height to the forested areas, which were delineated from orthophotography. The view-shed analysis was confined to the predefined study area.

Analysis was performed on the view sheds to determine which alternate corridor would least impact the local scenery. The acreage of the view shed, number of building centroids within the view shed, and the length of road frontage within the view shed were calculated.

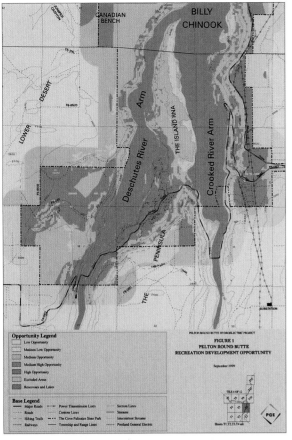

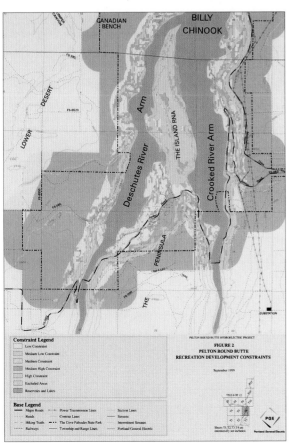

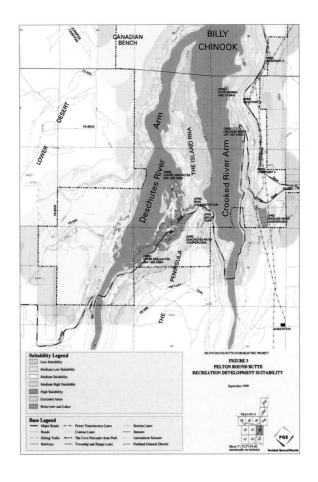

CH2M HILL
Redding, California

By Sarah Early

Contact
Sarah Early
searly@ch2m.com
Software
ArcInfo and ArcView GIS
Hardware
Windows NT
Printer
HP Design Jet 1055CM
Data Source(s)
Portland General Electric, Oregon
State Service Center, Prineville
Bureau of Land Management, and
EDAW
Map Type
Modeling/Analytical

Suitability mapping using ARC GRID was created for Portland General Electric to determine potential sites for new recreational areas. Data layers were gathered and set up in a matrix to show opportunities and constraints. Each layer received a predetermined ranking factor. These factors were used when converting the coverages to grids by weighing each new grid according to its ranking factor.

The grid max function was performed on all weighted grids. These weighted grids were normalized to produce an opportunity grid, a constraint grid, and a composite suitability grid. This sieving process was used to produce a more specified result instead of adding the grids together. This would allow very high opportunities/constraints areas to remain high, even if the area overlapped with several layers of lower opportunities/constraints.

The opportunity grid shows sites based on their potential for new recreational areas. The constraint grid shows sites based on their limiting factors for constructing new recreational areas. The suitability map shows sites based on their total composite suitability, showing areas with the highest potential for new recreational facilities.

A Study of Lexington, Kentucky, Growth Patterns

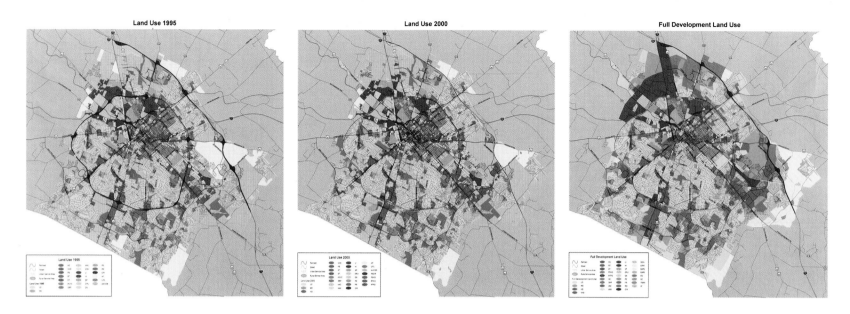

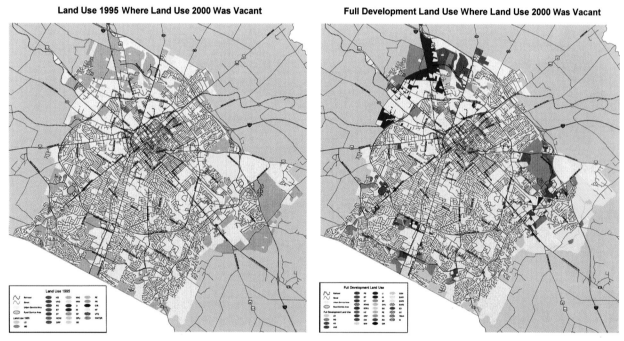

Lexington–Fayette Urban County
Government, GIS Section
Lexington, Kentucky

By Joseph Bell

Contact
Joseph Bell
jbell@lfucg.com
Software
ArcInfo and ArcView GIS
Hardware
Windows NT
Printer
HP DesignJet 1055CM
Data Source(s)
Local
Map Type
Decision/Planning

Lexington completed three land use studies—two inventories (1995 and 2000) and an expected full development (2020). The three coverages were integrated to produce a fourth coverage that was used to analyze land use changes.

Queries for 1995 land use equivalent to vacant were conducted to show the difference from land use 2000 and full development land use. The process was repeated for 2000 land use equivalent to vacant. The resulting maps display the land use changes between the three data sets.

This project was an evaluation of the land use inventory and analysis to determine the accuracy of projected land use to actual development. It concentrated on vacant land but can be produced using any land use category.

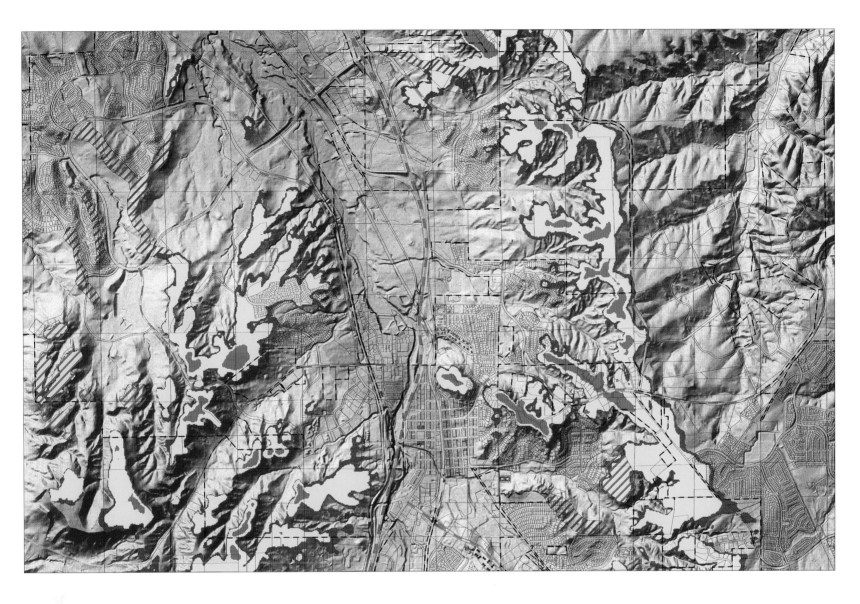

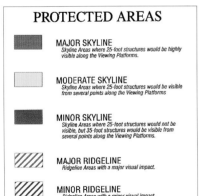

PROTECTED AREAS

MAJOR SKYLINE
Skyline Areas where 25-foot structures would be highly visible along the Viewing Platforms.

MODERATE SKYLINE
Skyline Areas where 25-foot structures would be visible from several points along the Viewing Platforms

MINOR SKYLINE
Skyline Areas where 25-foot structures would not be visible, but 35-foot structures would be visible from several points along the Viewing Platforms.

MAJOR RIDGELINE
Ridgeline Areas with a major visual impact.

MINOR RIDGELINE
Ridgeline Areas with a minor visual impact.

VIEWING PLATFORMS

PARCEL DATA

TOWN OF CASTLE ROCK BOUNDARY

The town of Castle Rock, Colorado, is the central part of one of the fastest growing counties in the country. In a short time, the town has had to deal with many issues related to the increased growth rate. To maintain a desirable standard of living, the town has been using GIS as an effective management tool.

A goal of the town has been to research and regulate growth and its impact on its natural and aesthetic resources. The study of the visual impact of development has become a key issue for new construction. To preserve its visual resources, Castle Rock initiated a program of protection for threatened areas. Skyline and ridgeline protection are now an integral part of the development review process.

Town of Castle Rock
Castle Rock, Colorado

By Joel Alexander

Contact
Joel Alexander
jalexander@ci.castlerock.co.us
Software
ArcInfo 8
Hardware
Windows NT
Printer
HP DesignJet 1050C
Data Source(s)
Town of Castle Rock
Map Type
Decision/Planning

Mapping the Urban Environment—Employment, Facilities Infrastructure, and Land Use

City of San Diego
San Diego, California

By Andrew Abouna

Contact
Andrew Abouna
d9a@sdcity.sannet.gov

Software
ArcInfo, ARCEDIT, and ARCPLOT

Hardware
Sun

Printer
HP DesignJet 1050C

Data Source(s)
San Diego Association of
Governments and City of San Diego

Map Type
Decision/Planning

San Diego is developing a Strategic Framework element within its Progress Guide and General Plan that will serve as a guidepost for general plan updates listing goals and objectives for San Diego's development.

The Progress Guide and General Plan helps the city plan for new facilities such as water and sewer pipes, roads, and affordable housing. The Strategic Framework element will reflect the past but incorporate the desires of today's San Diegans for accommodating growth. Raising the standard of living by attracting high-quality businesses and protecting the environment by implementing the Multiple Species Conservation Program are just two of its goals.

The San Diego Association of Governments (SANDAG) estimates that more than 450,000 new residents will be living in the city in 20 years. This is equivalent to the city's growth over the past 20 years with less than 12 percent of land available to develop.

The city has formed local committees to address several topics for the Strategic Framework such as economic prosperity, urban form and environment, neighborhood quality, regional issues, and public facilities and infrastructure. Public outreach in the form of joint seminars and meetings with the SANDAG, the County of San Diego, and other cities are planned and include sessions with local planning groups. These maps were produced by the planning department's GIS section for use by the citizen committees.

Stanford University
Stanford, California

*By Alan Cummings,
Kristina Seyer Smith, and Karen Stidd*

Contact
Kristina Seyer Smith
seyersmith@stanford.edu

Software
ArcView GIS, Adobe Illustrator,
Microsoft Access, and Oracle

Hardware
Windows NT

Printer
HP DesignJet

Data Source(s)
Stanford University maps and records
and field crew surveys

Map Type
Inventory

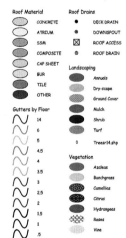

Stanford University Facilities Operations uses GIS technology to map the campus infrastructure, including campus buildings, utilities, and landscape features, to support facilities maintenance activities at the university. An Oracle database stores spatial attributes and pointers to specific spatial files on the server. The database was designed to migrate to a spatial database in the future. A single server currently supports an Oracle database and file storage. As applications and users increase, additional servers will be added.

ArcView GIS is used to view and analyze or create GIS data over an AutoCAD base map. Crews who maintain the campus roofs captured roof types, gutters, and drain locations. This map data can be used to calculate roof maintenance and replacement costs, and photos that document conditions in disrepair can be associated with mapped features. Area features represent general classifications of landscape types, which are used to manage labor, calculate capital costs, and estimate water use.

Web-based applications are also being planned to deliver interactive campus maps to the Stanford community that will provide information about a building's architecture or history, nearby parking lots, and phone numbers for departments located in the building. Intranet applications will provide additional features to desktops at Facilities Operations, Planning, and Environmental Health and Safety departments for managing campus operations.

Site Selection for Fire Station Development and Relocation

City of Wichita
Wichita, Kansas

By Mike Kollmeyer

Contact
Mike Kollmeyer
Kollmeyer_M@ci.wichita.ks.us

Software
ArcInfo 7.2.1 and 8.0.1, ARCEDIT,
ARC NETWORK™, ArcView GIS 3.2,
and ArcView Spatial Analyst 1.1

Hardware
Windows NT

Printer
HP DesignJet 2500CP

Data Source(s)
City of Wichita GIS, City of Wichita
Fire Department, Sedgwick County
GIS, and Metropolitan Area
Planning Department

Map Type
Decision/Planning

Population per Structure Fire

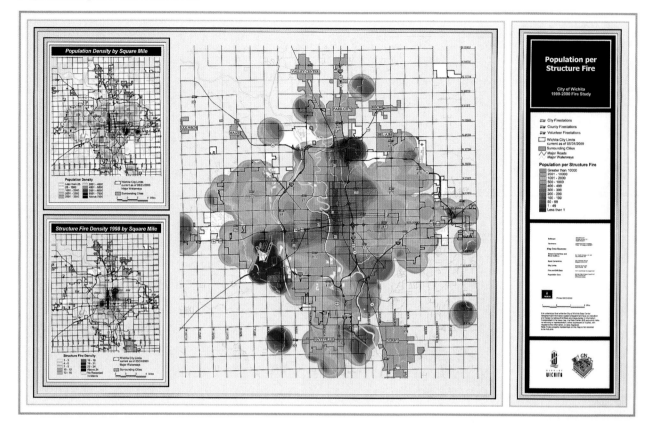

Historical Fire Station Locations

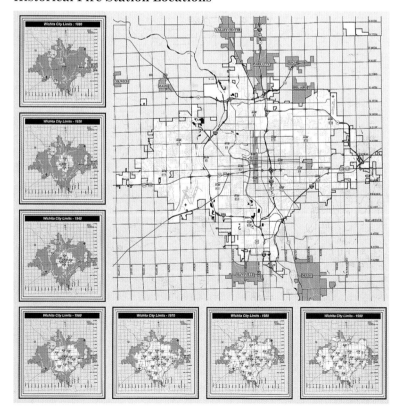

The rapid expansion of the city of Wichita has created some public safety issues for residents and businesses on the outskirts of town. The issue raised is whether the current fire stations can serve the expanded areas of Wichita in the required response time. Wichita city staff recommended a fire study to identify possible solutions for maintaining response times throughout the city as annexation and new development at the edge of town expands the service area.

GIS is a valuable tool for investigating and analyzing sites to locate and relocate fire stations. Response time allocation, future population projections, development patterns, and data from existing E-911 calls were analyzed in the GIS to identify fire station locations that would provide the best coverage to this growing city.

Structure Fire Response 1998

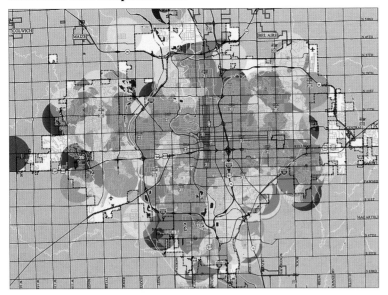

Structure Fire Incident Frequency 1998

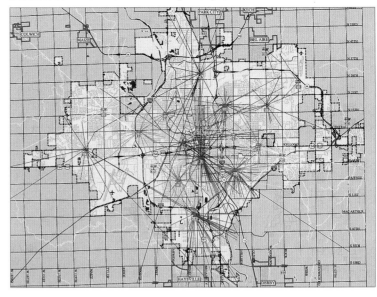

Projected Population Change 1997–2010

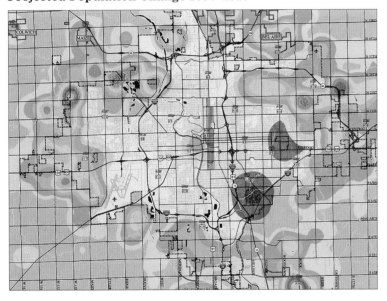

Proposed Urban Service Areas 2010–2030

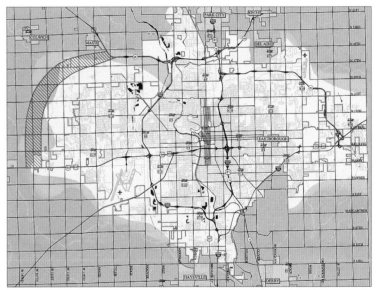

Fire Response: Six-Minute Coverage Area

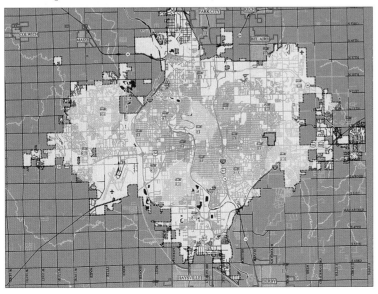

Fire Response: Eight-Minute Coverage Area

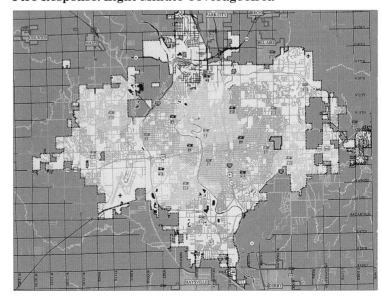

Fuel Beds of Ventura County

Ventura County Fire Protection
District
Camarillo, California

By Jim Kniss and Terry Raley

Contact
Jim Kniss
jim.kniss@mail.co.ventura.ca.us

Software
ArcView GIS 3.2 and ArcPress
Hardware
Desktop Computer PIII
Printer
HP DesignJet 1055
Data Source(s)
Sure Map! 1:100,000-scale topo map
and road layer provided by Ventura
County Public Works mapping
Map Type
Decision/Planning

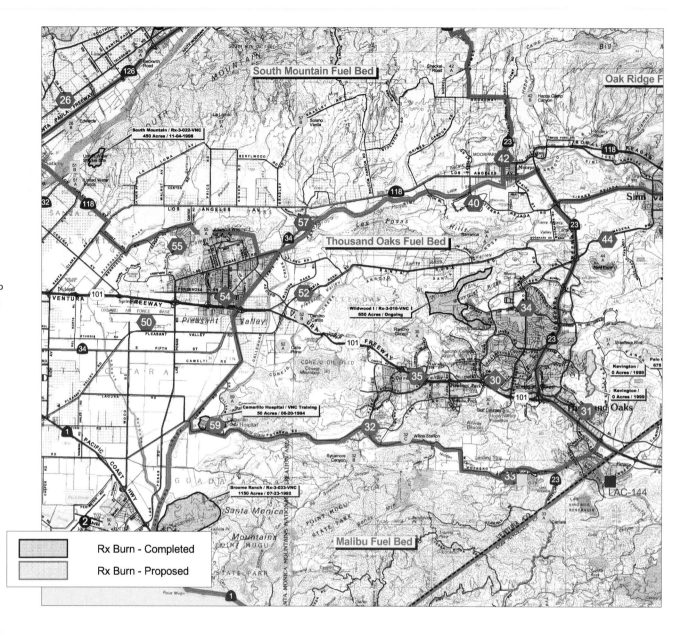

The Ventura County Fire Protection District is responsible for protecting nearly 1,000 square miles of urban and wildland interface property in Ventura County, California. Historically, wildfires have begun in the Simi Valley and Thousand Oaks area and made significant runs into populated areas, sometimes progressing as far as Malibu only to be stopped by the best firebreak in the world—the Pacific Ocean.

By analyzing its fire history for the past 100 years to determine patterns for when and where these fires occur, the district was able to divide the County into manageable fuel beds and develop work strategies to favorably modify the fuels in preparation for the next time a wildfire comes through these areas.

The district also developed preattack maps that outlined how the fire department would combat a wildfire in a given area. This analysis helped the district develop fuel beds using natural barriers such as ridgelines and river bottoms as well as man-made features (highways, developed land, and fuel breaks). With the county now sectioned into 10 distinct areas, separate plans were developed for each fuel bed using its unique features of land and fuel.

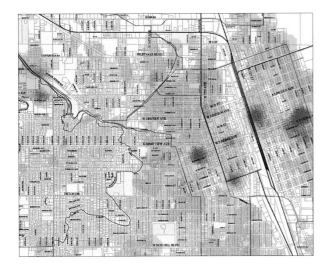

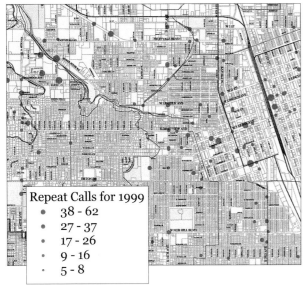

Repeat Calls for 1999
- 38 - 62
- 27 - 37
- 17 - 26
- 9 - 16
- 5 - 8

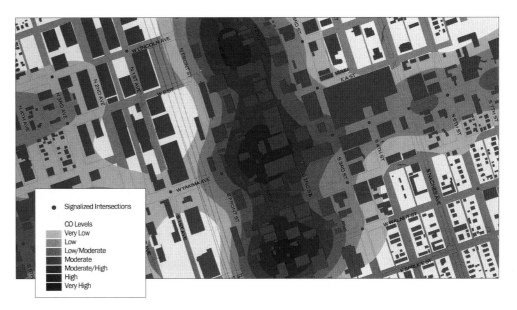

- Signalized Intersections

CO Levels
- Very Low
- Low
- Low/Moderate
- Moderate
- Moderate/High
- High
- Very High

FireView Maps

These FireView project maps were completed with contributions to the City of Yakima from ESRI Business Partners SunPro and the Omega Group. SunPro is a Yakima Valley software company that specializes in fire records management applications. The Omega Group is developing an ArcView GIS extension for fire departments called FireView.

FireView provides significant data reporting abilities for daily and routine tasks to the city of Yakima as it plans for the placement of a new fire station. Decision makers have access to FireView's analysis capabilities along with those of ArcView Spatial Analyst, ArcView Network Analyst, and the SunPro Fire records management database.

Carbon Monoxide Emissions Modeling by Intersection

Under the Federal Clean Air Act standards, Yakima is a Non-Attainment Area for Carbon Monoxide. Yakima proposes to reduce carbon monoxide emissions by improving traffic flow in the downtown business core.

Existing conditions were modeled using SYNCHRO 4.0 (Trafficware), a software product that evaluates the effectiveness of intersection signalization. Each of the 40 commercial business district intersections was modeled during evening peak hour traffic for existing conditions and optimized conditions.

The optimized plan identifies a 16.7 percent reduction in carbon monoxide emissions and a fuel savings of 137 gallons during evening peak hour. The emission values, both existing and optimized, were added to an intersection signal shapefile. Using ArcView Spatial Analyst, two maps were created to illustrate the emission patterns.

These maps will be submitted to the U.S. Environmental Protection Agency for approval and release of Congestion Management Air Quality funds to implement these improvements.

City of Yakima
Yakima, Washington

FireView Maps
By Jill Ballard, Corinne Choy, and Tom Sellsted
Carbon Monoxide Emissions Map
By Joan Davenport, Jill Ballard, and Tom Sellsted

Contact
Tom Sellsted
tsellste@ci.yakima.wa.us
Software
ArcView GIS 3.2, ArcView Spatial Analyst, SunPro Fire RMS, and FireView
Hardware
Windows NT 4.0
Printer
HP DesignJet 755CM
Data Source(s)
SunPro Fire RMS, SYNCHRO 4.0, and Yakima data layers
Map Type
Modeling/Analytical

Telecommunication Maps

Republic of Croatia VIPNET GSM Coverage

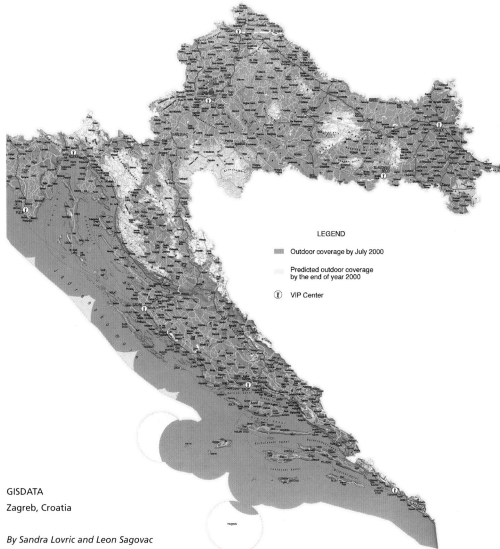

LEGEND

Outdoor coverage by July 2000

Predicted outdoor coverage
by the end of year 2000

VIP Center

GISDATA
Zagreb, Croatia

By Sandra Lovric and Leon Sagovac

Contact
Leon Sagovac
leon.sagovac@gisdata.hr

Software
ArcInfo 7.2.1, ARCPLOT, ARC GRID,
and Odyssey Network Planning Tool

Hardware
Windows NT and Sun UNIX
workstation

Printer
HP DesignJet 755CM

Data Source(s)
VIPNET GSM, GISDATA generalized
Digital Atlas of Croatia, and Croatian
Radiotelevision (HRT) digital
elevation model

Map Type
Inventory

City of Zagreb Phone Directory

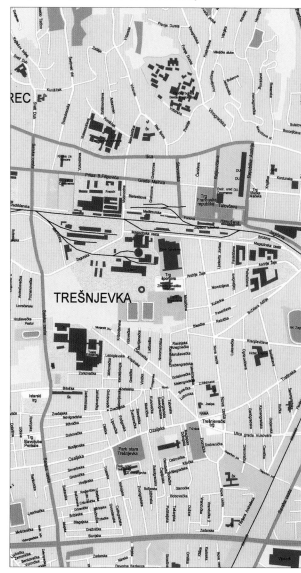

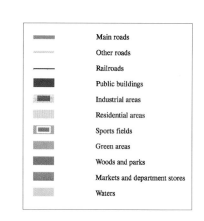

	Main roads
	Other roads
	Railroads
	Public buildings
	Industrial areas
	Residential areas
	Sports fields
	Green areas
	Woods and parks
	Markets and department stores
	Waters

VIPNET GSM is the first private global system for mobile communication (GSM) operator in Croatia. The 1:900,000-scale coverage map shows the areas where the current and planned VIPNET GSM signal can be captured by mobile phones, and it identifies VIPNET's main sales offices.

The prediction coverage is based on an extensive GIS database, which includes scanned and geocoded topographic maps, digital elevation models, clutter in 50- and 25-meter resolutions, and a vector database.

ARC GRID created the hue saturation value composite grid from the raster and hillshade coverage. To strengthen the coverage area and decrease the hillshade contrast, the sun altitude angle was set at 75 degrees.

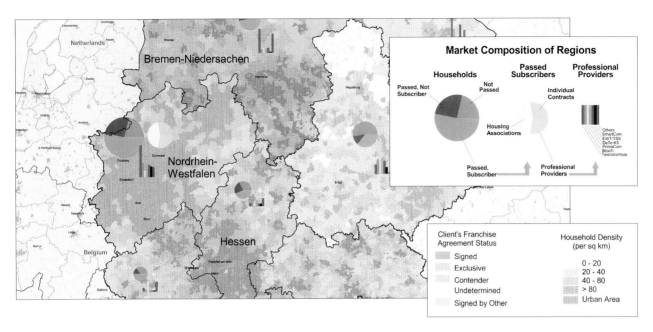

CH2M HILL, Inc.
Denver, Colorado

By Daniel Moreno

Contact
Daniel Moreno
dmoreno@ch2m.com

Software
ArcInfo 7.2
Hardware
Compaq Professional workstation
Printer
HP DesignJet
Data Source(s)
Digital Chart of the World
Map Type
Decision/Planning

Broadband Cable Franchise Opportunities in Germany

Telecommunications providers around the world are upgrading their systems to provide broadband cable services to residential and business customers. These services include traditional cable television, telephony, high-speed Internet data access, and two-way services such as video-on-demand. Providers compete for government-granted franchise licenses, and franchise opportunities vary in market size, market quality, and potential return on investment.

In this study for a global telecommunications company, franchise opportunities in Germany were evaluated for potential market opportunity. Each franchise region is symbolized by a pie chart that shows the number of households passed by existing cable systems and, of those households, how many are subscribers. A second pie chart characterizes the subscribers by type—housing associations, professional service providers, or individual subscribers. A bar chart displays the composition of the professional providers by company name, and household density by postal code area is shown as a gray tone backdrop.

In a fiercely competitive industry that demands huge capital investment, this kind of information helps telecommunications providers and their investors make intelligent business decisions.

Bringing Fiber Optics Telecommunications Services to Malaysia

Malaysia is one of the fastest developing and most prosperous countries in the Asia Pacific region. Population growth and rising disposable incomes in Malaysia have increased the demand for technology including advanced telecommunications services.

Maxis, a Malaysian wireless service provider, began an ambitious program to provide hybrid fiber-optic cable (HFC) services throughout peninsular Malaysia supplying households and businesses with cable television, video-on-demand, and high-speed Internet access.

CH2M HILL, an international consulting firm, was retained to plan, design, and construct the HFC system. CH2M HILL has used ArcInfo in each phase of the project to support market analysis, system design, construction, and operations and maintenance. The maps of Penang were produced as part of the planning process to identify market opportunities and develop a conceptual system design.

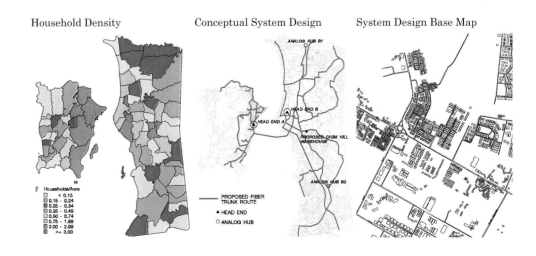

Household Density   Conceptual System Design   System Design Base Map

Regional Trails in King County

King County Park System and the
King County GIS Center
Seattle, Washington

*By Patrick Jankanish, King County
GIS Center, and Steve Johnson, King
County Park System
Contributors: Al Dams, Gavin Gray,
and Harkeerat Kang, King County
Park System, and Michael Jenkins,
King County GIS Center*

Contact

Patrick Jankanish

patrick.jankanish@metrokc.gov

Software

ArcInfo 7.1.2, ArcView GIS 3.2,
ArcView 3D Analyst, ArcView Spatial
Analyst, Adobe Illustrator 8 with
Avenza MAPublisher plug-in filters,
and Adobe Photoshop 5

Hardware

Compaq Professional AP400
workstation

Printer

HP DesignJet 3800CP with Fiery
X2-W DesignJet CP raster image
processor and four-color process,
sheet-fed, offset printing

Data Source(s)

King County GIS public data library
and King County Park System GIS

Map Type

Communication/Cartography

Regional Trails in King County is a reference map for the public that identifies the existence, locations, and routes of major hiking, biking, and equestrian trails in western King County. It comprises one full side of a text-photograph-map brochure, which it directly complements.

Trails and parks data sets were developed and provided to the King County GIS Center by the King County Park System GIS in shapefile format. Base map data, including point, line, and polygon shapefiles; annotation files; and a digital elevation model, were taken from the King County GIS public data library. Data was managed, and custom shapefiles were created within an ArcView GIS project that served as the digital map compilation platform.

All GIS data sets were imported into an Adobe Illustrator drawing file via the Avenza MAPublisher plug-ins for Illustrator. A georeferenced shaded relief TIFF image created with ArcInfo, ArcView 3D Analyst, and ArcView Spatial Analyst was combined in Adobe Photoshop with various background linear and polygonal map features copied from the Illustrator drawing to create a partial base map image. This composite image was imported into a drawing layer in Illustrator, and the final Adobe Illustrator drawing file with text and graphic embellishments was digitally color-separated to create lithographic film and printing plates for offset printing.

This process created a spatially accurate and graphically sophisticated product combining the best of what modern GIS and graphic illustration tools offer.

The Adirondack Forest Preserve

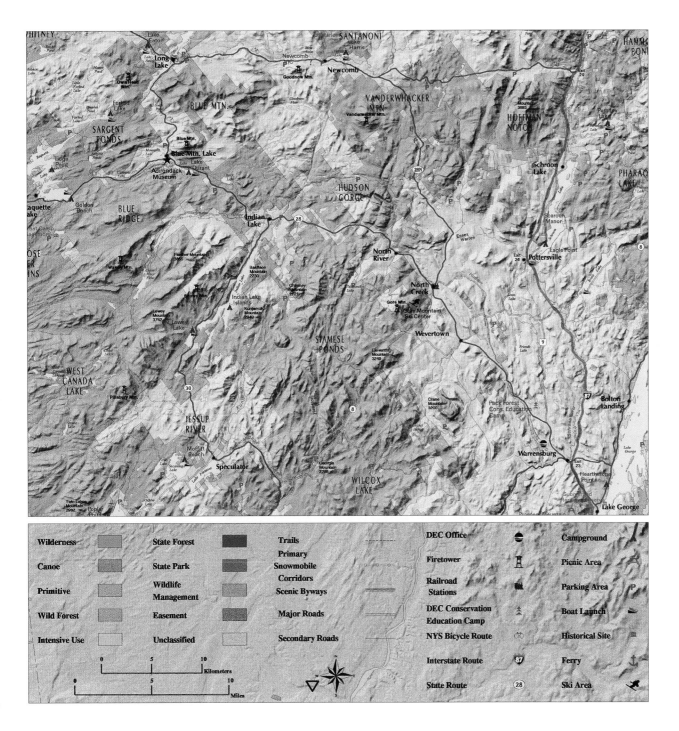

New York State Department of
Environmental Conservation
Albany, New York

*By Stephanie Diamond, Sheri Norton,
Kurt Swartz, and Karin Verschoor*

Contact
Kurt Swartz
kcswartz@gw.dec.state.ny.us
Software
ArcInfo 7.2.1 and ARCPLOT
Hardware
Sun Solaris 5.x UNIX workstation
Printer
HP DesignJet 2500CP
Data Source(s)
Digital elevation model and agency
developed data
Map Type
Communication/Cartography

The Adirondack Forest Preserve map was constructed to provide an overview of the distribution and diversity of outdoor recreational opportunities within New York's Adirondack Forest Preserve and to show the relationship of those opportunities to the scenic transportation corridors that traverse the region.

Created entirely in ArcInfo, using ARCPLOT and ARC GRID modules, this map culminates a long-term effort to communicate recreational information beyond traditional two-dimensional monocolor brochures that intensively portray selective areas. Following its first printing of 300,000 copies, the map is now in distribution, and a planned schedule will maintain current spatial information on a three-year cycle. Plans call for a series of detailed regional or specific activity brochures using the same shaded relief background and presentation formats from this map.

Flight Tracks for Asian Nations from Japan

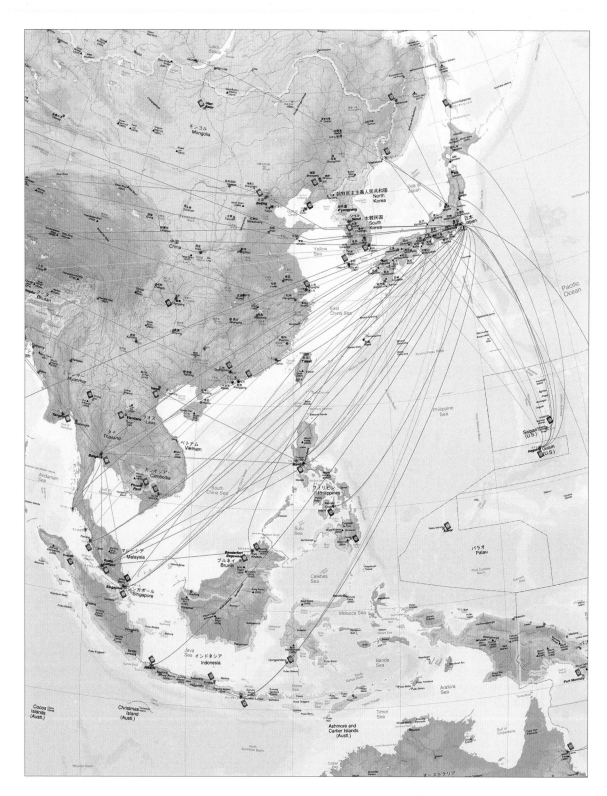

Hyogen Kenkyusho, Inc.

Tokyo, Japan

By Yoshiyuki Takei with K. Arai,
M. Basa, T. Namaumi, T. Takahashi,
and T. Wada

Contact

Mario Basa

mbasa@jcom.home.ne.jp

Software

ArcInfo 7.2, ArcSDE 8, ArcView
GIS 3.2, Maplex 3.3, Illustrator 8J

Hardware

Sun, Windows NT, and Macintosh

Printer

EPSON PM-9000C

Data Source(s)

Rand McNally World Database and
Hyogen Kenkyusho editorial data

Map Type

Communication/Cartography

As Japan diversifies its role in Asia, air transportation becomes more important. This map shows the status of air routes in Asia from Japan. Using Rand McNally's World Digital Database (WDDB) as the main data source, flight tracks were generated automatically. Several GIS applications use the WDDB data set as a base.

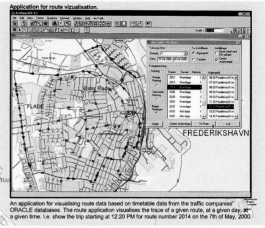

An application for visualising route data based on timetable data from the traffic companies' ORACLE databases. The route application visualises the trace of a given route, at a given day, at a given time. I.e. show the trip starting at 12:20 PM for route number 2014 on the 7th of May, 2000.

© Kort og Matrikelstyrelsen (A 47-01)

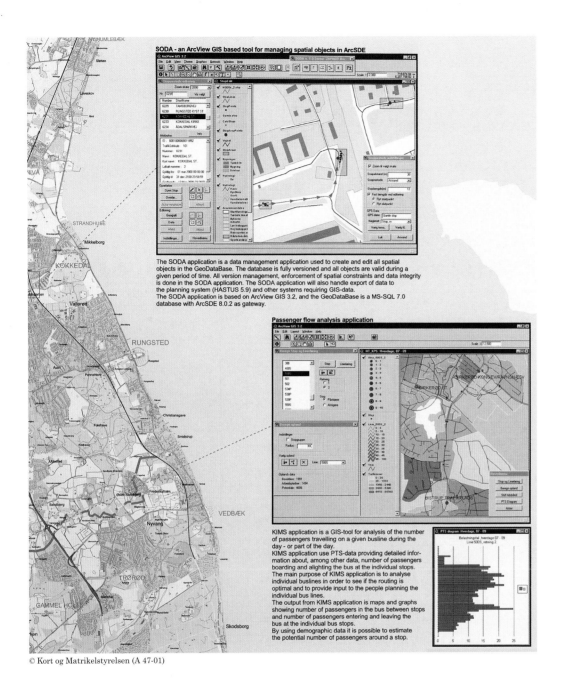

The SODA application is a data management application used to create and edit all spatial objects in the GeoDataBase. The database is fully versioned and all objects are valid during a given period of time. All version management, enforcement of spatial constraints and data integrity is done in the SODA application. The SODA application will also handle export of data to the planning system (HASTUS 5.9) and other systems requiring GIS-data. The SODA application is based on ArcView GIS 3.2, and the GeoDataBase is a MS-SQL 7.0 database with ArcSDE 8.0.2 as gateway.

KIMS application is a GIS-tool for analysis of the number of passengers travelling on a given busline during the day - or part of the day.
KIMS application use PTS-data providing detailed information about, among other data, number of passengers boarding and alighting the bus at the individual stops. The main purpose of KIMS application is to analyse individual buslines in order to see if the routing is optimal and to provide input to the people planning the individual bus lines.
The output from KIMS application is maps and graphs showing number of passengers in the bus between stops and number of passengers entering and leaving the bus at the individual bus stops.
By using demographic data it is possible to estimate the potential number of passengers around a stop.

© Kort og Matrikelstyrelsen (A 47-01)

Informi GIS A/S
Lyngby, Denmark

By Rasmus Holm Jensen and Michael Winther Larsen

Contact
Rasmus Holm Jensen
rasmush@informi.dk
Software
ArcInfo, ArcSDE, ArcPress, ArcView GIS 3.2, ArcView Network Analyst, ArcView Spatial Analyst, and ArcIMS®
Hardware
Windows NT and Dell Latitude PIII
Printer
HP DesignJet 755CM
Data Source(s)
Kort og Matrikelstyrelsen, Hovedstadsområdets Trafikselskab, and Nordjyllands Trafikselskab
Map Type
Automation

Informi GIS, the Danish distributor of ESRI software, provides GIS solutions and applications for Copenhagen Transport and the regional transportation companies. The applications range from data management tools to sophisticated analysis applications, and the number of users range from one to more than 20.

The maps show some of the applications developed for Copenhagen Transport and the regional transportation companies in Denmark. Applications that provide tools for automatic data generation, data management, and data analysis have been used since 1997 at Copenhagen Transport. The analysis applications range from passenger analysis applications where detailed information about passenger movement can be analyzed geographically to analysis and visualization of the speed of the buses in the road network.

In 1999, an application was developed and implemented for the regional transportation companies that features modules for maintenance of geodata, visualization and automatic generation, and aggregation of geographic data from Oracle timetable databases. The base data and cartography are part of the TOP10DK vector data set, which is provided by the National Survey and Cadastre of Denmark (Kort & Matrikelstyrelsen).

Olympic Mapping

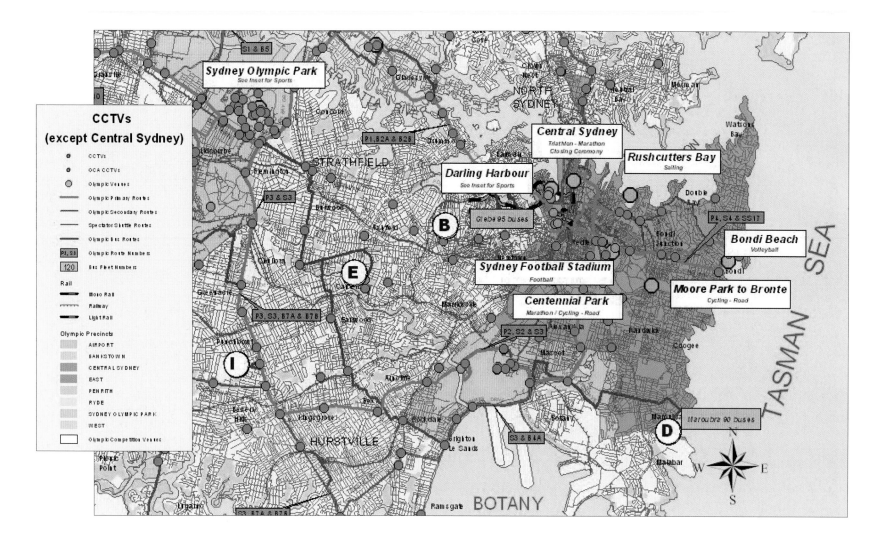

Roads and Traffic Authority (RTA) of
New South Wales (NSW)
Eveleigh, NSW, Australia

By Bryan Blake

Contact
Bryan Blake
bryan_blake@rta.nsw.gov.au

Software
ArcView GIS 3.2 and ArcPress

Hardware
Dell 410 Windows NT workstation

Printer
HP DesignJet 2500CP

Data Source(s)
Pacific Access centerline data, RTA
map data, spreadsheet, and
associated text

Map Type
Communication/Cartography

During the Sydney 2000 Olympics, the Transport Management Center was tasked to monitor and manage Sydney's road transport. The center produced daily competition maps displaying active daily venues; Olympic routes; primary, secondary, and park and ride bus locations; bus numbers; and Olympic precincts. Eight sets of 16 Olympic Day maps were produced for use in command centers around Sydney. There were 150 atlases produced with each containing 16 Olympic Day maps, two park and ride maps, a closed-circuit television map, and two variable message sign maps. Supporting spreadsheets and text were used as a strategic tool by Transport Management Center operations staff, traffic and precinct commanders in the field, and the New South Wales Police Service.

Incident Management System (IMS)

The Central Management Computer System is installed in Sydney and manages traffic in the Sydney arterial road network. There are plans to expand the system to cover the whole of New South Wales. The computers control devices such as variable message signs, motorway signaling units (known as variable speed limit signs), highway advisory radio, and advisory travel time signs.

The man/machine interface is implemented on PCs running under Windows NT with a Windows NT server (IMS computer system). This enables vector-based graphics, with geographic data extracted from the ArcInfo and ArcView GIS data sets that are held by the Roads and Traffic Authority of New South Wales.

This project was an award winner at OZRI 2000 in Melbourne.

B: Harold Park Paceway Park & Ride

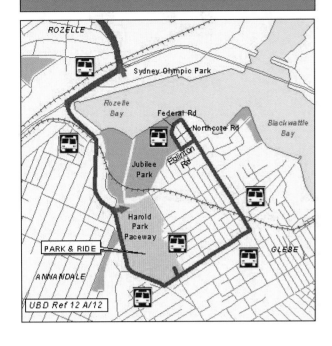

ROZELLE

Sydney Olympic Park

Rozelle Bay

Federal Rd

Northcote Rd

Blackwattle Bay

Jubilee Park

Egginton Rd

Harold Park Paceway

GLEBE

ANNANDALE

PARK & RIDE

UBD Ref 12 A/12

Olympic Daily Competition Venues

- ○ Olympic Venues
- Olympic Primary Routes
- Olympic Secondary Routes
- Spectator Shuttle Routes
- Olympic Bus Routes
- P3, S3 Olympic Route Numbers
- 120 Bus Fleet Numbers

Rail
- Mono Rail
- Railway
- Light Rail

Olympic Precincts
- AIRPORT
- BANKSTOWN
- CENTRAL SYDNEY
- EAST
- PENRITH
- RYDE
- SYDNEY OLYMPIC PARK
- WEST
- ▭ Active Olympic Competition Venues

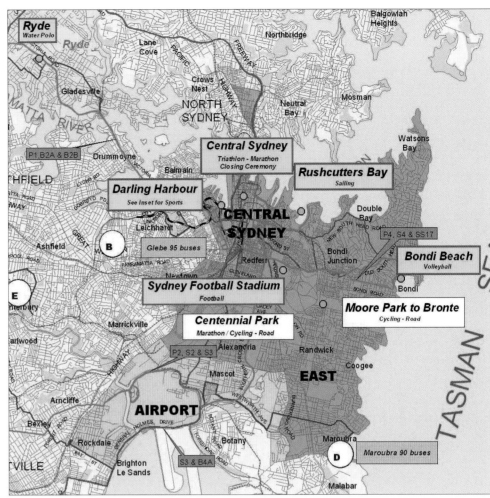

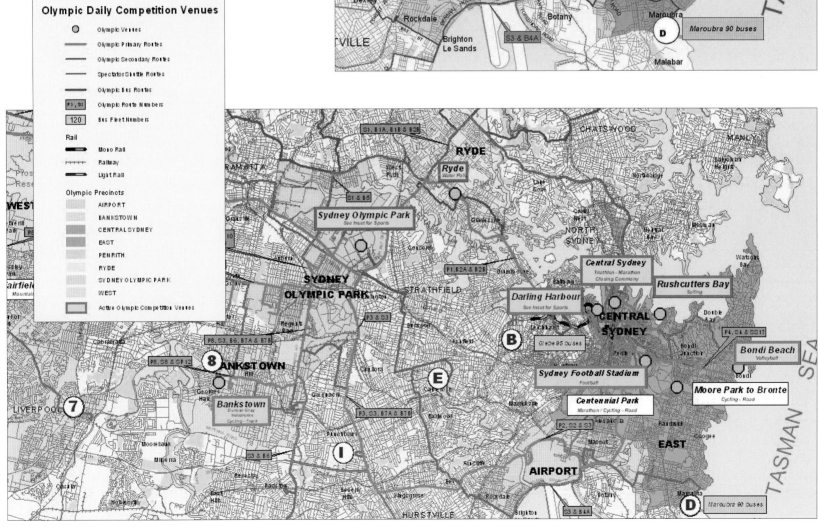

St. Louis, Missouri, Major Transportation Investment Analysis

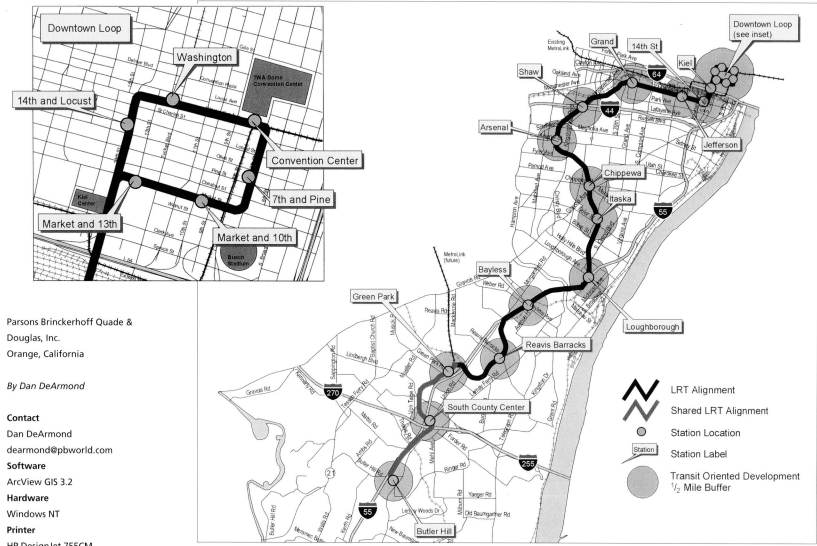

Parsons Brinckerhoff Quade &
Douglas, Inc.

Orange, California

By Dan DeArmond

Contact

Dan DeArmond

dearmond@pbworld.com

Software

ArcView GIS 3.2

Hardware

Windows NT

Printer

HP DesignJet 755CM

Data Source(s)

Parsons Brinckerhoff Quade &
Douglas, Inc.; East–West
Coordinating Council, and St. Louis,
Missouri

Map Type

Decision/Planning

The St. Louis Major Transportation Investment Analysis, Southside Study Area was a regional, multimode analysis that looked at light rail extension, major roadway improvements, and bus rapid transit alternatives designed to meet the long-term needs of the growing and shifting population and employment centers.

The goals and objectives of this study were developed from extensive corridor and systems planning studies carried out during the last 10 years and were defined based on planning and community involvement activities. Parsons Brinckerhoff Quade and Douglas, Inc., used GIS extensively throughout the process, from socioeconomic and demographic analyses in support of environmental justice to providing maps for public use at project scope meetings. Demographic information was compiled to evaluate the impact of the project on individuals and households in the immediate area, particularly the effects on minority and low-income communities.

Estimated population, employment, and zero-auto households contained within a one-half mile radius were recorded for each station. Using GIS with extensive community involvement, the team was able to quickly summarize the benefits and impacts of more than 20 variations of eight light rail and bus rapid transit alignments and station scenarios.

Environmental Justice Factors in the Conceptual Level Design of a Transit Project

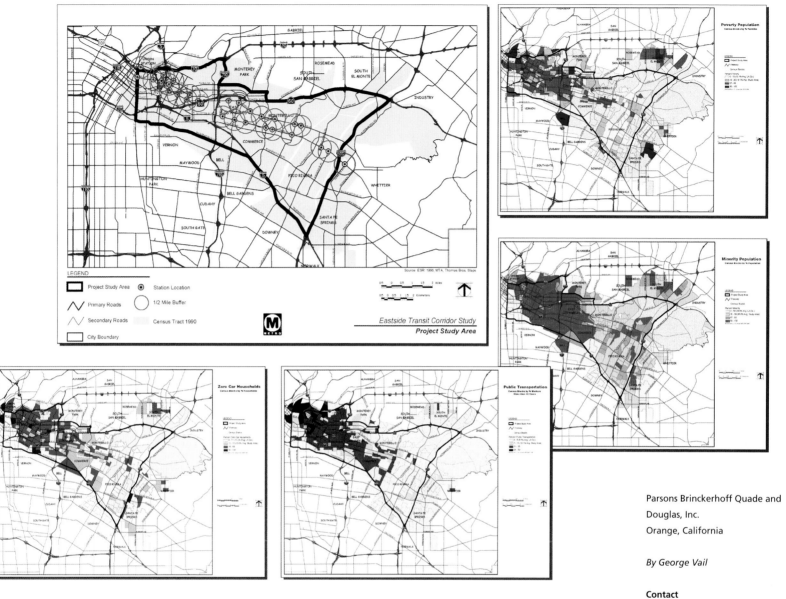

Parsons Brinckerhoff Quade and
Douglas, Inc.
Orange, California

By George Vail

Contact
George Vail
vail@pbworld.com

Software
ArcInfo 7.2 and ArcView GIS 3.2
Hardware
Windows NT
Printer
HP DesignJet 755CM
Data Source(s)
Parsons Brinckerhoff Quade and
Douglas, Inc.; Thomas Bros. Maps®;
and 1990 U.S. Census
Map Type
Decision/Planning

In 1998, Los Angeles County voters approved a measure that prohibits the Los Angeles County Metropolitan Transportation Authority (LACMTA) from using county sales tax revenues to finance planning, design, construction, or operation of any new subways. As a result, LACMTA is conducting a major investment study (MIS) to examine transit alternatives from heavy rail transit (HRT), to light rail transit (LRT), to bus rapid transits (BRT).

The communities of Boyle Heights and East Los Angeles feel that the siting and construction of the five freeways in that area have adversely affected them. The eastside transit project extension would serve these residents who travel throughout Los Angeles County and beyond. The improved transportation will create greater access and increase economic development in the region.

U.S. Census data from 1990 and projected socioeconomic and demographic data sets were used to analyze the population groups that would be served at each station, affected during the construction, and displaced due to construction and require mitigation. Using GIS and extensive community involvement, the project team quickly reduced more than 28 station alternatives down to eight for the locally preferred alternative, which will receive further engineering and environmental analysis.

Transportation Maps

Employees and Population by Traffic Analysis Zone

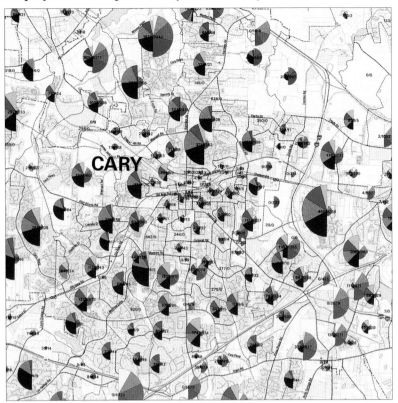

Abu Dhabi Transportation and Roads Inventory Program

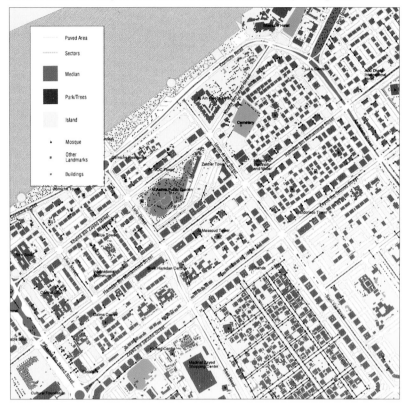

Parsons Transportation Group
San Jose, California

By Eric Coumou

Contact
Eric Coumou
eric.coumou@parsons.com
Software
ArcInfo 8
Hardware
Sun Solaris 2.7
Printer
HP DesignJet 2500CP
Data Source(s)
Wake County, North Carolina; U.S.
Census Bureau; and Municipality of
Abu Dhabi
Map Type
Decision/Planning, Inventory, and
Modeling/Analytical

Employees and Population by Traffic Analysis Zone

By using relative-sized dots for residential and employee populations, county planners can easily see present traffic patterns and predict future problems. Each traffic analysis zone (TAZ) for Wake County, North Carolina, is displayed on this map and represented by a dot. The left semicircle is sized relative to the population in the year 2000, and the right semicircle is sized relative to the number of employees in the year 2000.

To display future growth, each TAZ is further broken down to show relative levels of either population or number of employees for the years 1995, 2005, 2015, and 2025. Parsons Transportation Group is gathering this data as part of the Wake County Automated Data Systems Project.

Abu Dhabi Transportation and Roads Inventory Program

Abu Dhabi, capital of the United Arab Emirates, has undergone considerable growth due to the development of its oil reserves. Transformed from scattered huts built in the sand dunes to a modern metropolis of high-rise towers in just 30 years, Abu Dhabi is an urban planning challenge. The purpose of the Transportation and Roads Improvement Project (TRIP) is to develop a comprehensive transportation plan.

A GIS has enabled large amounts of data to be displayed and analyzed. For modeling, the outputs from ArcInfo are put into traffic modeling software, and the results are input back into ArcInfo. Census data is being collected by door-to-door surveys, and those results are going into the GIS database.

Currently the GIS contains a huge library of data, which enables planners to design roads, intersections, and buildings for the future Abu Dhabi Emirate.

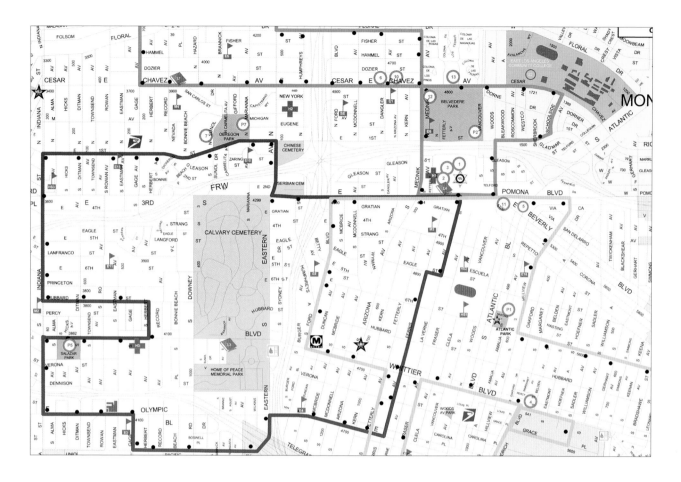

Los Angeles County Department of Public Works, Mapping and Property Management Division, Mapping and GIS Services Section, GIS Services Unit
Alhambra, California

By Larry Halweg, P.E., and Farid Hamedy

Contact
Larry Halweg, P.E.
lhalweg@dpw.co.la.ca.us
Software
ArcInfo 7.2.1, ArcView GIS 3.1, Adobe PhotoShop 5.5, and Adobe Illustrator 8.0
Hardware
Dell Precision 410 workstation with Windows NT 4.0 SP 6, Apple G3 PowerBook with Macintosh OS 8.6, Sun SPARC 20 workstation with UNIX Sun/Solaris Open Windows 3.4, and Microtek 6400XL color scanner
Printer
HP DesignJet 3500CP
Data Source(s)
Thomas Bros. Maps, digitized routes, geoprocessed points, scanned photographs, GIF/BMP/TIFF images, WordPerfect document, and Microsoft Excel spreadsheet
Map Type
Communication/Cartography

This community guide map was installed in more than 50 bus shelters to serve daily bus riders and tourists in the East Los Angeles community. When the East Los Angeles community planners were developing the shuttle routes and stations for their shuttle system, they needed a multifunctional map that could guide the riders and inform people about accessible community services along the shuttle routes.

A county supervisor's office contacted the Department of Public Works Programs Development Division to coordinate constructing the shelters and producing the maps. The Programs Development Division asked Mapping and Property Management Division's GIS Services Unit to produce the maps, which were approved and posted on time in spite of tight deadlines, budget constraints, and procurement issues. The Department of Public Works' mission was definitely met with this project—providing public works services in a responsive, efficient, and cost-effective manner. The laminated four-by-six-feet map and the accompanying bilingual foldout schedule/map were placed in bus shelters for public use.

The Department of Public Works contracted the bus shelter construction and poster printing with Eller Media Company. This map was a marvel to create. The GIS Services Unit produces all hard-copy maps using UNIX-based ArcInfo. Eller Media Company uses a Macintosh for all graphics production and a large, digital press for poster printing. The challenge was to integrate these diversified platforms, take a UNIX-based map, and transform it into a Macintosh-based digital deliverable as required by Eller. Windows NT-based ArcView GIS 3.1, Adobe PDF Writer, and Adobe Illustrator 8.0 were the bridge.

There is more information about the shuttle service including an Adobe Acrobat PDF version of the map at http://elanet.co.la.ca.us/shuttle/shuttle.html.

Water Utility Maps

Water Distribution Map

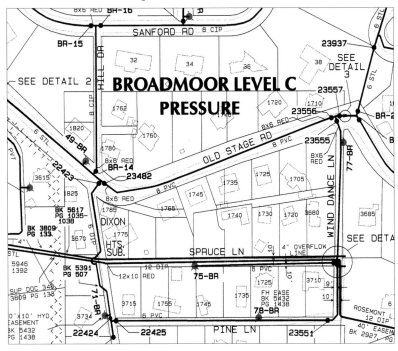

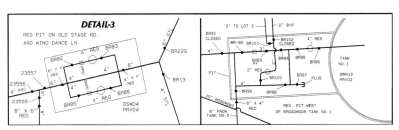

Static Water Pressure Analysis/Water Main Leak Location

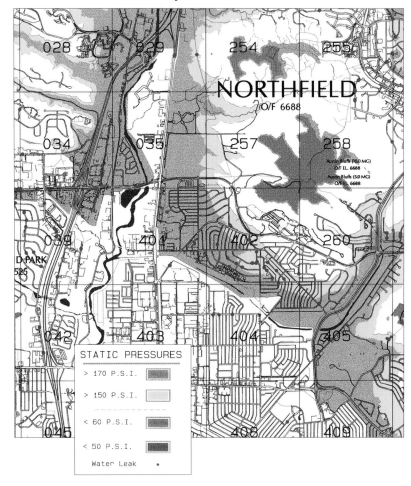

Colorado Springs Utilities
Colorado Springs, Colorado

By David Krenek

Contact
David Krenek
dkrenek@csu.org
Software
ArcInfo
Hardware
Solaris
Printer
HP DesignJet 1055
Data Source(s)
Colorado Springs Utilities data
Map Type
Communication/Cartography

Water Distribution Map

This is a typical water map book sheet within the city. ArcInfo created the map plot, and it is updated daily as changes to the system occur. The scale is typically 1:200, but some plots are created at 1:400.

Major land base features, such as buildings, streets, lots, and streams, are shown in different line types. The main water features are shown in solid bold and designed (not built) features are shown as dashed. All annotation was hand placed to minimize interference with other features. To ensure that valve and hydrant numbers are always readable, the area under the annotation is clipped. The map book sheets are used in the field either as hard-copy sheets or as digital images on laptops.

Static Water Pressure Analysis/Water Main Leak Location

This map displays the City of Colorado Springs water pressure boundary system. It illustrates where in the city high- and low-static water pressure exist. Because of the city's hilly terrain, the water system consists of 26 different pressure zones. There is a 2,500-foot elevation difference from one end of the city to the other.

Yellow represents pressures from 150 pounds per square inch (psi) to 170 psi. Brown represents areas of the city where the pressure is greater than 170 psi. The red and blue areas represent pressures that are less than 60 psi. The extreme pressures in the city cause a number of problems for the Water Resources Department. High water pressure contributes to water main breaks while low-pressure areas generate customer complaints.

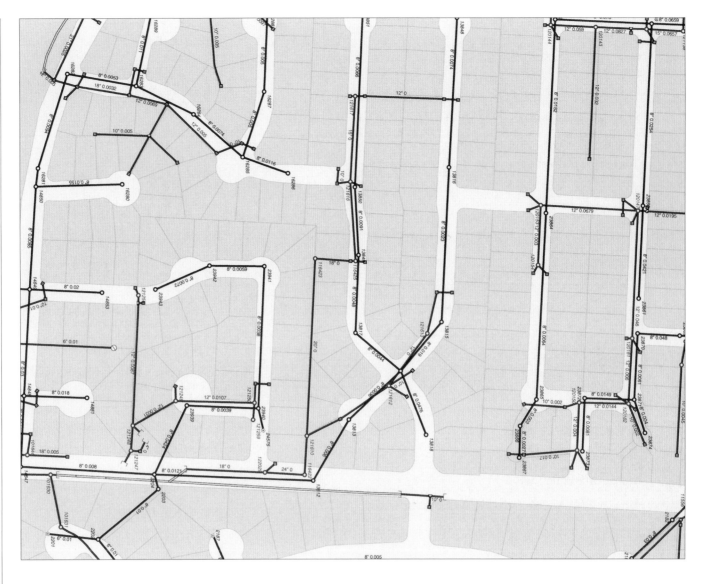

The Unified Sewerage Agency (USA) was one of the first implementers of an Arc 8 geodatabase. ESRI produced this plot to demonstrate the plotting and reporting capabilities within ArcMap. The map shows USA's sewer and storm water pipes and facilities as they exist in a geometric network inside an enterprise geodatabase. The text within the view uses the dynamic labeling function within ArcMap. Columns of text were created using the report function on USA's invert-elevation and upstream-elevation fields and inserted onto the map layout. The key map was created using an additional data frame specified as an extent rectangle for the main section of the map.

This map was also produced to demonstrate that data can be seen both spatially, as the pipe diameters and slope label text shows, and in report format with the invert-elevation and upstream-elevation fields. The elevations are linked to the spatial features by the Junction IDs, which are displayed on the map.

Unified Sewerage Agency (USA)
Hillsboro, Oregon

By Karyn Senneff

Contact
Karyn Senneff
ksenneff@esri.com

Software
ArcMap™

Hardware
Compaq SP 700

Printer
HP DesignJet 2500CP

Data Source(s)
USA and Washington County

Map Type
Communication/Cartography

INDEX

INDEX

Edited by
Nancy Sappington

Design by
Doug Huibregtse and Sue Morasco

2001 ESRI Map Book
Copyright © 2001 ESRI
All rights reserved
Printed in the United States of America

Front and Back Cover
Digital Shasta—Applying GIS Technology to Volcano Hazards (pages 54–55)

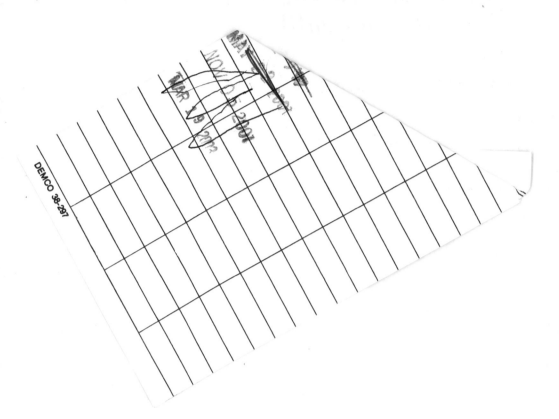